SXR207 Physics by Experiment
Science: Level 2

The O

A Practical Handbook

Prepared for the Course Team by Stuart Freake

SXR207 Production Course Team

Course Team Chair	Keith Hodgkinson
Author	Stuart Freake
Course Manager	Sue Messham
Course Secretary	Tracey Woodcraft
Editor	Peter Twomey
Graphic Designers	Steve Best, Sarah Hofton
Photographer	Mike Levers
Software development	Will Rawes
Technical support	Sandra Mills, Roger Bence, Martin Percy
Consultant	Alan Cayless

This book has drawn freely from earlier versions of practical handbooks that were produced for Open University Science Foundation Courses (S100, S101, S102) and introductory physics courses (S271 *Discovering physics* and S207 *The Physical World*). We gratefully acknowledge the work of the many members of these course teams who contributed to the development of these handbooks over the last 30 years.

The course SXR207 *Physics by Experiment* also includes a one-week residential school, where students perform a variety of physics experiments. This experimental work is largely based on experiments that were developed for the S271 *Discovering physics* residential school, and the contributions of members of the S271 Course Team are gratefully acknowledged.

The Open University, Walton Hall, Milton Keynes MK7 6AA

First published 2001. Second edition 2008.

Written, edited, designed and typeset by the Open University.

Printed and bound in the United Kingdom by The Alden Group, Oxfordshire.

ISBN 978 0 7492 1448 7

This text forms part of an Open University course, SXR207 *Physics by Experiment*. Details of this and other Open University courses can be obtained from the Course Reservations Centre, PO Box 724, The Open University, Milton Keynes MK7 6ZS, United Kingdom: tel. +44 (0) 1908 653231; e-mail ces-gen@open.ac.uk

Alternatively, you may visit the Open University website at http://www.open.ac.uk where you can learn more about the wide range of courses and packs offered at all levels by the Open University.

To purchase this publication or other components of Open University courses, contact Open University Worldwide Ltd, The Berrill Building, Walton Hall, Milton Keynes MK7 6AA, United Kingdom: tel. +44 (0) 1908 858785, fax +44 (0) 1908 858787, e-mail ouwenq@open.ac.uk

2.1

SXR207 PHbk i2.1

A PRACTICAL HANDBOOK

1 Introduction

Physics is an observational and experimental science that investigates the workings of the physical world. It encompasses observations on the immense scale of the Universe, experiments on the infinitesimal scale of quarks, and everything in the intervening range. Since the time of Galileo, one of the earliest experimenters, physicists have designed telescopes and used them to investigate astronomical bodies, from the moons of Jupiter to the most-distant known quasars in the Universe. Astronomical observations now use the whole range of the electromagnetic spectrum, from radio waves through to γ-rays. The data that astronomers collect provide evidence to answer questions about the formation of the Solar System, the existence of planetary systems around other stars, and about the origins of the Universe in the Big Bang.

At the other end of the distance scale, large teams of physicists at laboratories like CERN design complex accelerators to produce beams of particles with very high energies that they smash together. By analysing the debris from these collisions, physicists construct theories of quarks and other fundamental particles and of the way that these particles interact.

Between these two extremes, physicists in universities and in industries throughout the world carry out laboratory-scale experiments to advance our understanding of fundamental science and to apply it in new devices. Large numbers of physicists are employed in the important fields of semiconductors and superconductors, liquid crystals and magnetic materials, lasers and quantum optics, medical imaging and electron microscopy, to name but a few.

So experiments have played, and continue to play, a crucial role in developing our understanding of the physical world. If you want to understand and get a feel for the role of experiments, perhaps the best way is to be involved with them yourself — to do some physics experiments. This is a major reason why physics students are required to do experimental work as part of their courses — as an introduction to the process of experimentation.

The experiments that you do as a student will have many stages. These may include the initial planning of the experiment, making and recording observations and measurements, their analysis and interpretation, assessing the uncertainties in the final result, reaching a final conclusion, and then the reporting of the experiment. These stages parallel what a research physicist might go through in a research project. By following similar processes as a student, you will be learning to think like an experimental physicist, and this will be valuable if you go on to work as an experimentalist. However, even if you don't, it will give you insights into tackling practical problems that will be valuable in many areas of work or home experience. It will also enable you to evaluate the experiments reported by others.

Various other benefits come from doing physics experiments as a student. Many experiments demonstrate important concepts and phenomena of physics, and seeing a phenomenon or measuring an effect can make it more real and memorable. Doing experiments develops a wide range of skills that you will use in other areas besides physics — everything from planning to problem solving, from analysing data to presenting results. Experimental work also gives an opportunity to work collaboratively with other students, and this can be a powerful learning experience, as well as developing interpersonal skills.

1.1 Structure of the book

In this book, we will be discussing a variety of aspects of experimental work, with the aim of providing a sound basis for tackling physics experiments. This does *not* mean that we will be providing information about using specific measuring instruments or techniques, or advice about particular experiments — the range of instrumentation and experiments available in the modern physics laboratory is too vast and varied to make that appropriate. Instead we will concentrate on the generic aspects of physics experimentation: planning for an experiment, keeping records of what you do, estimating the uncertainties in measurements, numerical and graphical analysis of data, and producing a written report on an experiment.

We start, in Section 2, by discussing preparation and planning for an experiment. A little time invested in this stage can pay dividends in the quality of your results and the efficiency with which they are obtained. Section 3 is about keeping records of your experiments — recording what you do in an experiment, how you do it, what you observe and measure, the analysis and interpretation of your results, and so on. Without any records to refer back to, you are likely to find that the details of how you did the experiment and any conclusions that you draw from it will be rather ephemeral and soon forgotten. We provide some guidelines for maintaining a laboratory notebook, and you may find it helpful to refer to these guidelines when doing your experiments.

Sections 4 to 6 then tackle an important topic for any experimenter who makes measurements: how reliable are the results? Physicists make the reliability of a numerical result explicit by quoting an uncertainty alongside the result; for example, a mass might be quoted as (75.4 ± 0.3) g. Section 4 gives some examples of how uncertainties in measurements arise, and Section 5 discusses how you can make quantitative estimates of their magnitude. Section 6 then shows how uncertainties in different parts of an experiment can be combined to provide an estimate of the uncertainty in a final result.

Most experiments involve numerical analysis of the data, and Section 7 gives a few brief guidelines that should help with this. Data analysis may involve graphs, and graphs are frequently used by physicists as a powerful tool for displaying and interpreting results; Section 8 deals with this topic in some detail. Both data analysis and graph plotting have been revolutionized in the last decade by the ready availability of graphic calculators and computers, and Section 9 indicates a few of the ways that these are used in experimental work.

For practising physicists, carrying out an experiment and analysing the results is generally of limited value unless those results are then communicated to other scientists. This communication would generally be achieved by publishing the results in a scientific journal or reporting them at a conference. Section 10, therefore, offers some guidelines on how to produce a clear and complete report on your experimental work.

2 Preparing for an experiment

When faced with a new experiment, you may be tempted to assemble the equipment and make some measurements as soon as possible, perhaps in a rather haphazard fashion. This temptation is particularly strong in a teaching laboratory, where a fixed period is available for the experiment. The message in this section is that you should avoid succumbing to this temptation. Before launching into an experiment, it is worth spending a little time thinking about the purpose of the experiment, and planning how you will carry it out. Approaching an experiment in a systematic way will usually mean that you use the time that is available more efficiently.

An essential part of the preparatory stage is to make sure that you are clear about the goals of the experiment. Are you aiming to measure the value of something, confirm or deduce a relationship between different variables, or simply observe a particular phenomenon? It will be helpful to read any background information that is provided about the theory that underpins the experiment or about the experimental techniques and measuring instruments that will be used. This will often be provided as part of the notes and instructions for the experiment, but you may also need to refer to other course materials or books. Also, many experiments are designed to develop specific laboratory skills and, if you are made aware of this, you should make sure that you devote suitable time and effort to these particular skills.

Then you need to consider what measurements or observations you will make, and under what conditions. As an example, suppose that you were asked to investigate the dependence of the period of a simple pendulum on its length, mass and amplitude. You would have to decide:

- over what ranges of the three variables you should take measurements — when trying to deduce a functional relationship, it would generally be advisable for each variable to change by a factor of ten or more;
- how many values of each variable should be used — four or five values might be enough to establish the functional form of a relationship if the measurements were reasonably precise;
- how values of the variables should be distributed — equally-spaced values are often the best bet when there is a smooth variation in the measured quantity, but more values are needed where there are more dramatic changes, or perhaps where the precision is lowest;
- how the measurements should be organized so that the dependence of the period on each individual variable can be deduced — selecting arbitrary combinations of the length, mass and amplitude would be an inefficient and possibly ineffective way to proceed; much better to keep two of the variables constant (e.g. length and mass) and investigate how period depends on the third (e.g. amplitude), and then to investigate the dependence of period on each of the other variables in a similar way;
- whether other possible variables (such as thickness of the string or air temperature) need to be kept constant.

Another issue to think about is the *precision* required in the experimental measurements: for example, do you need to measure the length of a pendulum to the nearest centimetre, to the nearest millimetre or even to the nearest 0.1 millimetre? This may determine your choice of measuring instrument or measuring technique, and it will affect the number of measurements that you make. It is also important to think about how the uncertainties in the individual measurements contribute to the overall uncertainty in the final result. This will allow you to concentrate your efforts on improving those measurements that make the largest contribution to the overall uncertainty.

You should consider how you will analyse and display the data that you collect in the experiment. What tables do you need to draw up for recording your data? Do you need to leave space for extra columns in data tables to compute other quantities that are derived from the data? What graphs will you need to plot as you are collecting data?

Before starting any experiment, you need to consider any potential safety hazards and the precautions that can be taken to reduce risks. Health and safety legislation places responsibilities on everyone who works in a laboratory. The people supervising work in a teaching laboratory are required to carry out risk assessments for the experiments and procedures, and they have a responsibility to inform students about the hazards and about the precautions that should be taken. Students then have a responsibility for taking the necessary precautions. However, it is good practice to think for yourself about the hazards of each experiment that you do: are there possible dangers from use of electricity (mains electricity or high voltages), from equipment or materials at high or low temperatures, from chemicals, from use of lasers, from moving objects, and so on?

A final reason for spending some time on the planning stage is that you will have a better idea of what is involved in the experiment, and this should allow you to divide your time appropriately between the different stages.

2.1 Preliminary experiments

It is often useful to carry out a preliminary experiment before getting down to the 'real' measurements. This can serve a number of purposes.

(a) You can familiarize yourself with how the apparatus works and with the controls that have to be adjusted during the experiment. Your first few measurements in an experiment are likely to be less reliable than later ones, so it is better to get the necessary practice in a preliminary experiment. This is particularly important if a sequence of operations has to be carried out, perhaps in a short time, requiring manipulative skills that need some practice. You can also ensure that any equipment that needs frequent adjustment is positioned in such a way that the adjustments are easy to make, and that measuring instruments are sited so that it is easy to read their scales and displays. You will also want to ensure that there is a convenient space for the laboratory notebook that you will use to record your measurements.

(b) A preliminary experiment allows you to discover how quickly a measured quantity changes (if there is some time dependence), or the way in which one variable depends on another; you can then plan your measurements accordingly. You can also ascertain which ranges on the measuring instruments will be most appropriate, and can practise reading the scales or displays.

(c) If you are doing an experiment with other people, then you can decide who will do what during the experiment. Roles that might be allocated include making various adjustments to the controls during the experiment, reading instruments, recording data, analysing data and plotting graphs, and so on. However, you should avoid splitting tasks in such a way that the uncertainties in your measurements are increased. For example, if one person throws a 'start' switch and shouts 'now', while a second person starts a timing device, then the uncertainty in the timing is likely to be greater than if one person operates both the switch and the timer.

(d) You can make some estimate of the uncertainties in the measurements, so that you are able to concentrate your efforts on reducing the uncertainties that have greatest effect on the final result.

(e) Preliminary measurements can give an indication of the time required for various parts of the experiment, so that you can plan to allocate the available time appropriately.

Of course, you must avoid being carried away with your planning and preliminary experiments. You should only spend enough time on them to give you confidence that you know how the experiment works and that you have a plan for carrying it out. However, your plan should be flexible, since the odds are that you will need to modify it as the experiment proceeds.

3 Keeping records

Physicists may spend months or even years on research or development projects. During that time, they will plan experiments, design apparatus, make measurements and observations, and analyse data. There may be many separate parts to a project, and a complex project may involve a large team, so that information needs to be shared. There will be times when apparatus does not work initially and needs to be redesigned, when a variety of different approaches to analysing the data are tried, or when parts of the investigation are unsuccessful so that different approaches have to be devised. Imagine trying to do all of this without keeping good records of what has been done!

In addition, physicists have to write reports, publish papers and give presentations at conferences, and this may be done months or even years after experimental work was carried out. It is therefore essential to have an accessible, reliable and complete record of the work on which these communications can be based. Moreover, if experiments lead to patentable results, then it may be important to have a record of what was done, and when, in order to establish precedence; a well-maintained laboratory notebook can provide the appropriate evidence.

Therefore, keeping a laboratory notebook is an essential skill for an experimental physicist. However, the skills that you develop by maintaining a laboratory notebook are transferable to many other contexts. Software developers need to document the code that they develop, otherwise they will spend hours trying to remember what each part of a program does when they have to modify or update it. Journalists need to keep records of interviews and sources of information so that they can revisit them if necessary at some future time.

However, using a laboratory notebook will have benefits for you in the shorter term too. As a student, you may well be asked to produce a report of an experiment that you have done. This will be much easier to do if you have a written record of the important information in an easily located place. You may get different results from other students for an experiment, and want to compare the records in your notebooks to see how these differences have arisen. Or you may do an experiment that involves similar experimental techniques or similar data analysis to an experiment that you have done previously; if you can refer back to records in your notebook you may avoid having to start again from scratch.

3.1 Guidelines for keeping records in a laboratory notebook

The notes provided for student experiments usually give instructions — sometimes in a fair amount of detail — on how to set up the apparatus, what data must be collected, which graphs should be plotted, and so on. This rather prescriptive approach is dictated by various constraints on time, place and available equipment. It means that you are very often freed from having to make detailed notes of experimental procedure, since there is clearly little point in writing down in your notebook information that can easily be referred to elsewhere. However, you should keep a careful record of *your* observations and data, and make notes of specific details of your experiment that are not described in the instructions.

There are few rigid rules about how to keep a record of your laboratory work, but we can provide the following guidelines.

(a) Use a bound notebook The best way to ensure that you retain a permanent record of your experimental work is to record details in a *bound* notebook. Books that contain both lined paper and graph paper are ideal. If an ordinary lined-paper notebook is used, graphs should be stuck, or stapled, in as soon as they are drawn. It's not good practice to use loose sheets of paper — they can (and usually do) get lost. Punched sheets and a ring binder are not really a satisfactory compromise, as pages can easily become detached or shuffled.

Always record your comments and data directly in your notebook. Resist the temptation to jot down bits of information on odd sheets of paper with the intention of neatly copying it into your notebook later. This is an incredible waste of time, and it brings the risk of errors in copying. Also, don't be tempted to record your data in pencil with the intention of going over the data in ink later 'when you are sure that it's correct'. There will always be the temptation to erase data, and this is very bad practice (see point (i) below).

Your first attempts to record details of your experiments in your notebook will probably be rather messy (mine certainly were!), but your records will improve, as you become more experienced.

(b) Make your record clear and concise Your laboratory notebook should constitute a complete and clear record of your work. It should contain the information needed to produce a report (or scientific paper), which you might not begin to write up until months after carrying out the experiment. It should provide sufficient detail for you, or for someone else, to repeat the measurements or the data analysis. This means that it must be clearly laid out, and self-explanatory. Cryptic comments, or data without headings or units, may seem adequate at the time you record them, but will very soon become meaningless. However, you should make your notes reasonably concise; there is no need for complete sentences where a short phrase can convey the necessary information.

(c) Record the date Each experiment in your notebook should be dated, and there may be situations in which it is important to record the time at which events occurred or measurements were made. There will undoubtedly be occasions when you come back to your notebook and add additional information, re-analyse data or reinterpret results, and it is useful to date any later entries that you make to distinguish them from the original record.

(d) Space out your entries Paper is cheap, so space out the entries in your notebook so that you can come back and insert additional comments or additional information in the most logical and convenient place. It is generally a good idea to start the record of each experiment at the top of a new page.

(e) What should you record? A bold title at the start of the record will make it easy to locate. If you then make a brief note of the main aims of the experiment, you will have an accessible reminder of what the experiment was about when you refer back to it.

In Section 2 you were advised to spend some time at the start of an experiment planning how to make measurements, how many measurements to make, at what values of the independent variables, and so on. Your plans, and comments explaining the rationale behind them, should be recorded in your notebook. Don't worry that your plans may change — you can explain why they change in your notebook too.

If you do some preliminary experiments to help this planning process, note down the results and the lessons you draw from them. In particular, make a note of any changes to the way you plan to do the main experiment as a consequence of the preliminary measurements, or note that the preliminary experiments confirmed that your initial plans seemed appropriate.

There is no need to repeat information that is in the instructions, but you should note the conditions prevailing during the measurements, and any modifications you make to the suggested procedure. Note, also, identifying details of the equipment and measuring instruments that you use (for example, their serial numbers), since if your results turn out to be anomalous you might need to check for faults. You should record any special precautions that you take and any checks on procedures and measurements. Odd, unexpected, or plain inexplicable observations may turn out to be of crucial significance, so be sure to make a note of any such events or results. Write down all information, *as you go along*. Most of it will be irretrievable once you have left the laboratory.

(f) Diagrams In many situations, a labelled sketch diagram of the equipment and how it is laid out will be helpful, and can save you writing a lot of words. No great artistic or drafting skills are required for these diagrams, as the examples in Figure 3.1 show. Again, there is no point in reproducing diagrams from the instructions for the experiment.

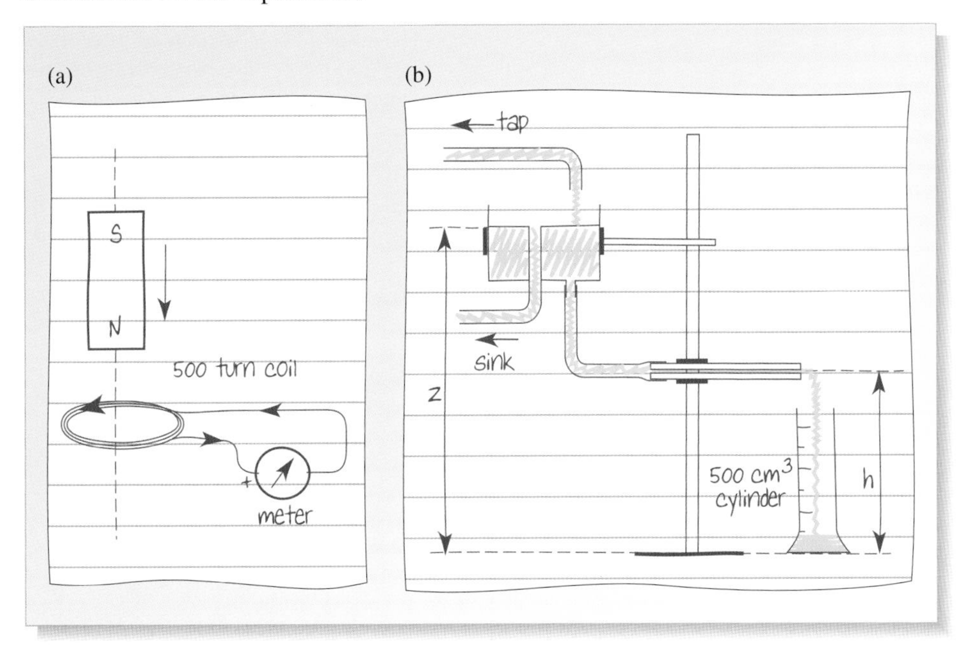

Figure 3.1 Simple freehand sketches can convey a lot of useful information about an experiment. (a) A sketch of an electromagnetic induction experiment, showing the relationship between the motion of the magnet and the direction of the induced current. (b) A sketch of the apparatus for determining the viscosity of water by measuring the flow rate through a capillary tube.

(g) Recording data in tables When making a series of measurements of the dependence of one quantity on another, it is generally best to record the results in a table (see the example in Figure 3.2). Make sure that you include column headings that indicate the quantities that are being recorded and the units in which they are measured — Box 3.1 explains the rationale for the way in which this is normally done. It is usually helpful to insert a caption above a table to indicate what measurements are recorded there, and to note any special conditions that apply to these measurements.

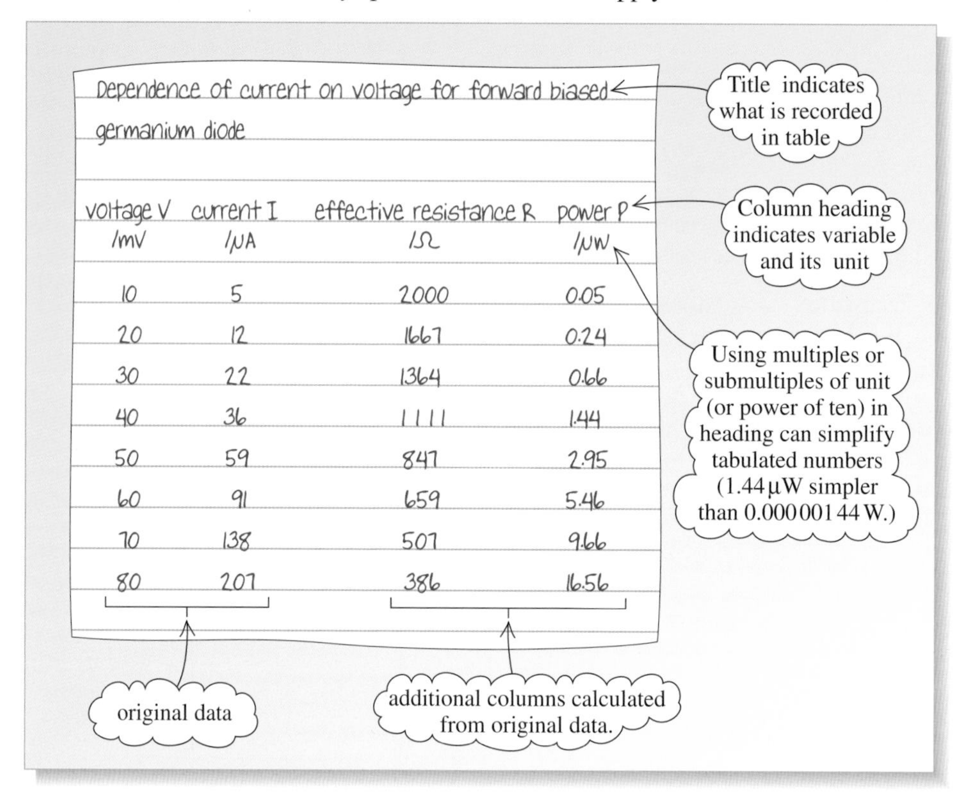

Figure 3.2 The first two columns in this table were recorded during an experiment in which the current through a diode was measured at eight different values of the applied voltage. The space to the right of these two columns was left blank for possible subsequent calculations. After completing the measurements, the experimenter added the two additional columns on the right for effective resistance and power. If there had been no space beside the original table, the experimenter would have had to copy the table elsewhere — possibly introducing transcription errors.

You will frequently need to manipulate your tabulated data in order to calculate other quantities. For example, having measured and recorded the voltage V and current I, as shown in the first two columns of the table in Figure 3.2, you may need to calculate values of the effective resistance, $R = V/I$, or of the power dissipated, $P = IV$. Recording the results of subsequent calculations is much easier if you have left space beside the original table so that you can add extra columns, as shown on the right in Figure 3.2.

Of course, sometimes you will be recording a measurement, or a series of measurements, of a single quantity, and so a table will not be appropriate. You then need to include a clear statement of what is being measured alongside the measured value: for example, 'Ambient temperature = 21 °C'. (See also point (j) below.)

Box 3.1 Units in tables, graphs and equations

There is a good deal of confusion about how the unit of a physical quantity should be represented in table headings, on graph axes, or when the value of that physical quantity is substituted into an equation. Yet the international convention we use is both straightforward and, once the basic principles have been understood, quite logical. The most important rule to remember, and from which all the rest follow, is that whenever a symbol is used to represent a physical variable — say t to represent time, or d to represent distance — then that symbol is deemed to incorporate a numerical value *and the physical unit attached to that value*. By making this assumption, it then becomes possible to write identities such as

$$t = 5\ \text{seconds} \qquad (3.1)$$

or

$$d = 10\ \text{metres} \qquad (3.2)$$

since the units balance on both sides of the equation. (If t only represented the *number*, we would have to write t seconds = 5 seconds, which is something we never do!)

It now follows that, if we divide both sides of Equation 3.1 by seconds, and both sides of Equation 3.2 by metres, we have

$$\frac{t}{\text{seconds}} = 5 \qquad (3.3)$$

$$\frac{d}{\text{metres}} = 10 \qquad (3.4)$$

where the quantities on both sides of these equations now have no units. And this is really how you should interpret table headings and graph axes like those shown in Figure 3.3. By dividing the variable by the unit, the entries in the table, or the quantities on the graph are pure numbers. So point A on the graph in Figure 3.3b is at t/seconds = 5, i.e. at t = 5 seconds. By all means read this 'slash' notation as meaning 't in the unit of seconds' if you find this easier, but always keep in mind that the 'slash' really does represent a true division.

Occasionally, tables are drawn up as in Figure 3.4. This format is still logical — the table reads directly: distance = 10 m, or time = 15 s etc., but notice that the unit must now be included with *every* entry in the table. However, the format in Figure 3.3 is generally neater, simpler and minimizes the amount that you have to write.

Substituting numerical values into equations follows exactly the same logic as above. Suppose you have the equation

$$d = vt,$$

where d represents distance, v represents speed, and t represents time. The first point to note is that the units on either side of this equation are balanced, because the symbols are deemed to incorporate the units. But now suppose you are asked to calculate the distance travelled when the speed is 2 metres per second, and the time is 10 seconds. All you need to remember is that when you substitute the values, *you must substitute the units as well*; only in this way will you keep the units on either side of the equation balanced. So, substituting for the speed, you can write

$$d = (2\ \text{m s}^{-1})t,$$

and then substituting for the time, you can write

$$d = 2\ \text{m s}^{-1} \times 10\ \text{s}$$

or

$$d = 20\ \text{m}$$

(where the s has cancelled the s^{-1}).

You will see that we always include units in our numerical working in this book, particularly in the answers to the Questions, and you should be careful to do this in your own numerical calculations.

(a)

distance/metres	time/seconds
0	0
10	5
20	10
30	15

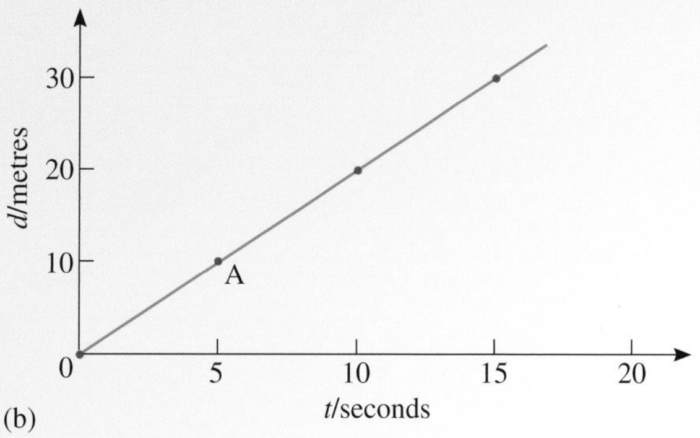

(b)

Figure 3.3 (a) Units in table headings; (b) units on graph axes.

distance	time
0 m	0 s
10 m	5 s
20 m	10 s
30 m	15 s

Figure 3.4 A less common, though still logical, way of completing a table.

(h) Always record raw data Record in your notebook the measurements *as read directly from the instruments*. Don't perform arithmetic operations on the instrument readings in your head and then only record the results of this mental arithmetic. Corrections, such as allowing for zero errors, converting to a different unit or applying calibration corrections, should be done *after* recording the raw data. For example, if you need to subtract a background reading from a series of measurements, record both that background reading and the individual measurements; then list the 'corrected' measurements in a separate column. Any arithmetic slips will then be traceable.

(i) Correcting errors in your notebook If you do discover an error in your notebook, simply cross out the original record and insert the new one beside it, with a note (or footnote) explaining the reason for the correction. You will not be marked on the number of errors in your notebook, and having a record of places where you have made mistakes can be excellent for learning. Also, it is possible that you will realize subsequently that a result that you thought was erroneous is actually evidence for an important effect that you had been unaware of. There have been many occasions in the history of science when data was ignored or discarded because it was thought to be erroneous or anomalous, only to be rediscovered later by another scientist and shown to be evidence for a new effect.

(j) Recording uncertainties in measurements Physicists normally estimate the uncertainty in a quantitative result from the uncertainties in individual measurements. We will be discussing uncertainties in much more detail in Sections 4 to 6, but in the context of your laboratory notebook, the following important point should be stressed. You should record your assessment of the uncertainties in all of the quantities that you measure. In the case of the temperature measurement referred to at the end of point (g), you might record 'Ambient temperature = 21 °C ± 0.5 °C'.

You should also note anything that might have a bearing on the reliability of the measurements, for example, a meter that oscillates before settling down; the order in which measurements are made; the time interval between measurements; and so on.

(k) Data analysis Data handling — in particular, combining uncertainties in a quantity or quantities and using graphs — is covered in Sections 6 to 8 of this book. However, bear in mind that all of the steps of your data analysis and calculation should be recorded in your notebook. Your calculations will be easier to follow when you return to them later if you lay them out neatly, with plenty of space between steps, and if you insert comments explaining the steps.

(l) Conclusions and critical reflections Your final conclusions and any comments about the interpretation of your results should be noted. If appropriate, you should comment on how well your result agrees with published data or theoretical results, and suggest explanations for any differences. Also, record any thoughts that you have about how successful the experiment was, what its limitations were, how it might be improved and what you might do differently if you repeated the experiment. Reflecting critically on your experimental work in this way should enable you to improve your skills as an experimental physicist!

Question 3.1 Figure 3.5 displays a page from a student's laboratory notebook. What improvements would you suggest that the student could make? ■

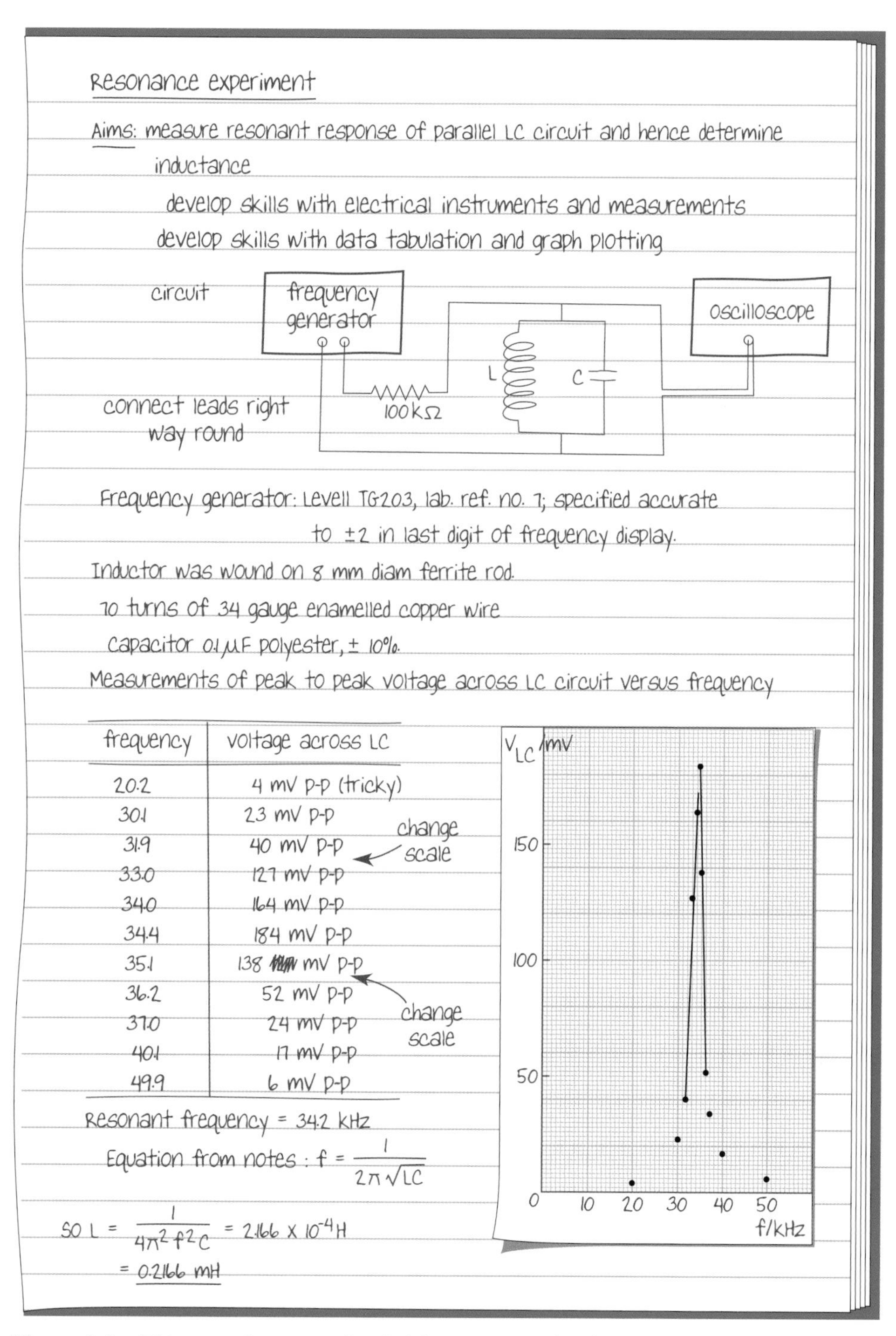

Resonance experiment

Aims: measure resonant response of parallel LC circuit and hence determine inductance

develop skills with electrical instruments and measurements

develop skills with data tabulation and graph plotting

circuit

connect leads right way round

Frequency generator: Levell TG203, lab. ref. no. 7; specified accurate to ±2 in last digit of frequency display.

Inductor was wound on 8 mm diam ferrite rod.

70 turns of 34 gauge enamelled copper wire

capacitor 0.1 μF polyester, ± 10%.

Measurements of peak to peak voltage across LC circuit versus frequency

frequency	voltage across LC
20.2	4 mV p-p (tricky)
30.1	23 mV p-p
31.9	40 mV p-p ← change scale
33.0	127 mV p-p
34.0	164 mV p-p
34.4	184 mV p-p
35.1	138 mV p-p ← change scale
36.2	52 mV p-p
37.0	24 mV p-p
40.1	17 mV p-p
49.9	6 mV p-p

Resonant frequency = 34.2 kHz

Equation from notes : $f = \frac{1}{2\pi\sqrt{LC}}$

so $L = \frac{1}{4\pi^2 f^2 C} = 2.166 \times 10^{-4}$ H

$= 0.2166$ mH

Figure 3.5 This page from a student's laboratory notebook has a variety of shortcomings. Question 3.1 asks you to suggest possible improvements.

4 Experimental uncertainties

Measured values of physical quantities are never exact. There are always uncertainties associated with measurements, and it is important to assess the magnitudes of the uncertainties and to quote them alongside the measured values. So if a physicist did an experiment to determine the acceleration due to gravity at a particular location, then the form in which they would quote their result would be $g = (9.85 \pm 0.06)\,\mathrm{m\,s^{-2}}$. This means that their best estimate of the value of g is $9.85\,\mathrm{m\,s^{-2}}$, and their confidence in this value is quantified by the uncertainty $\pm 0.06\,\mathrm{m\,s^{-2}}$, so the value could be as high as $9.91\,\mathrm{m\,s^{-2}}$ or as low as $9.79\,\mathrm{m\,s^{-2}}$.

The value of the uncertainty conveys important information about a result, as you can see by considering the following questions.

● Two physicists make measurements of g at the same place but using different experimental methods. One quotes the result as $(9.78 \pm 0.02)\,\mathrm{m\,s^{-2}}$ and the other as $(9.84 \pm 0.06)\,\mathrm{m\,s^{-2}}$. In which result would you have more confidence?

❍ The quoted uncertainty in the result of the first experiment is one-third of that obtained in the second experiment. This indicates that the first experiment was carried out more carefully, or used better equipment, or used a better technique, so it would be reasonable to have more confidence in the first result. (This assumes, of course, that the quoted uncertainties are realistic!)

● The value of g is measured at two different places by the same experimenter, using the same technique. She finds that at location A the value is $(9.78 \pm 0.03)\,\mathrm{m\,s^{-2}}$ and that at B the value is $(9.82 \pm 0.03)\,\mathrm{m\,s^{-2}}$. Do these results indicate that g is different at the two locations?

❍ The answer is: not necessarily. Her results are consistent, for example, with the value of g being $9.80\,\mathrm{m\,s^{-2}}$ at both locations, since this value falls within the uncertainty ranges for both experiments. (The difference between the two values might motivate the experimenter to devise a more precise measuring technique. Had the uncertainties been $\pm 0.01\,\mathrm{m\,s^{-2}}$, then the results would provide strong evidence that g was different at the two locations, since the uncertainty ranges would have been clearly separated.)

● An Earth scientist uses a model of the internal structure and composition of the Earth to *calculate* a value for g at a particular location. His result is $(9.84 \pm 0.04)\,\mathrm{m\,s^{-2}}$, whereas the experimentally *measured* value of g at that location is $(9.823 \pm 0.002)\,\mathrm{m\,s^{-2}}$. Is the result for g predicted by the model consistent with the experimental measurement?

❍ Yes, the prediction and the measurement are consistent, since the uncertainty ranges overlap. (However, the uncertainty associated with the experimental measurement is much smaller than that associated with the prediction from the model, and this might spur the Earth scientist to refine the model so that it can give a more precise prediction to compare with the measured value.) ■

These three examples illustrate the importance of attaching an uncertainty to a measured value.

Uncertainties or errors?

You will find that the uncertainties discussed above are referred to by many scientists as *experimental errors*, or simply *errors*. However, this terminology can be confusing, because in everyday usage an error is a mistake — something that is wrong. Even in the best scientific experiments, carried out with the utmost care by the most skilled experimenters, there will be an uncertainty in a measured value; the negative connotations of error seem to make the use of the term inappropriate here.

Another reason for avoiding the term 'error' in this context is that quoting an error of $\pm x$ in a measurement implies that there exists a definite correct value. However, in many experiments this is not the case. For example, you may be measuring a quantity that fluctuates with time, so that each measurement gives a different value. Alternatively, you may be measuring the diameter of a wire and find that it has small variations along its length. In cases like these, the scatter of the measured values indicates the variability of the quantity being measured.

For these reasons, we will talk about uncertainties rather than errors in this course. However, you should keep in mind that many authors, out of deference to convention, use the term error instead.

4.1 How do uncertainties arise?

It is useful to be aware of the various types of uncertainties that can occur in experimental measurements, and to understand how and why uncertainties arise. This knowledge will enable you to recognize (and take steps to minimize) the uncertainties in the measurements that you make. Whilst we cannot give a comprehensive list of all sources of uncertainty in physics experiments, the categories outlined below should provide a framework for considering what the uncertainties might be in a particular situation.

Note that real errors (mistakes) are *not* included in this discussion. This is not because they never occur, but because they are impossible to predict or quantify. Everyone will misread a scale on occasions, transpose digits when writing down a number, or incorrectly apply a calibration factor to a measurement. However, you can generally avoid these errors by careful attention to the procedure that you are following and by always checking measurements and calculations.

(a) Uncertainties caused by lack of skill This kind of uncertainty is one that almost falls into the 'mistake' category. The ability to start or stop a stopwatch to coincide with an event that is being timed is a skill that can be developed. Similarly, you can learn how to minimize the *parallax* uncertainties that can arise when reading a scale (Box 4.1). Other uncertainties of this type can arise from misaligning a measuring instrument, or simply not setting it up correctly. In general, such uncertainties become smaller as you gain more experience with experimental work. Also, modern instruments are generally designed to minimize such uncertainties — for instance, digital meters eliminate the possibility of parallax uncertainties associated with reading the position of a needle on a scale (Figure 4.2c).

In Box 4.1 you will meet the first emboldened term 'parallax'. Terms that are emboldened in the text are ones that you should be able to define without reference to the book.

Box 4.1 Parallax uncertainties

Observing parallax

Hold a book in one hand at arm's length, as shown in Figure 4.1, and hold a ruler horizontally in the other hand, midway between the book and your eyes. Close one eye, tilt your head to the left and note the approximate position of one of the vertical edges of the book on the ruler scale. Then with one eye still closed, and with the book and the ruler fixed, tilt your head to the right.

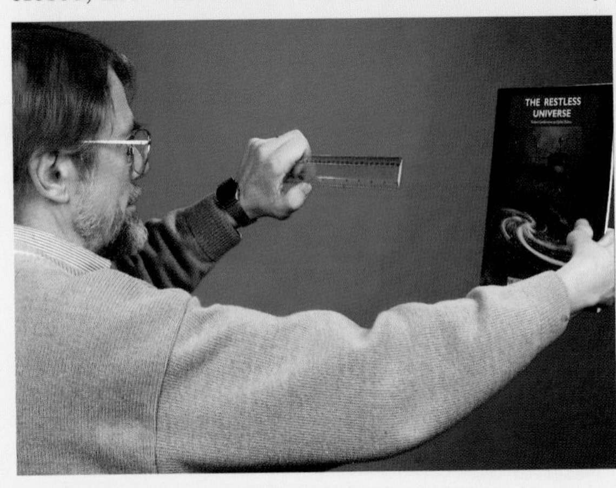

Figure 4.1 A simple way to observe parallax.

- What happens to the apparent position of the edge of the book as measured by the ruler?

❍ When your eye moves to the right, the apparent position of the edge of the book moves towards the right-hand end of the ruler scale. Conversely, moving your eye to the left causes the apparent position of the edge of the book to move to the left of the scale.

- Repeat your observation with the ruler closer to the book, tilting your head about the same amount to the left and to the right as before. How do these observations compare with your first observations?

❍ The change in apparent scale reading is smaller when the ruler is closer to the book, and increases as the distance between ruler and book increases. ■

This dependence of the apparent position of an object on the position of the observer is known as **parallax**.

The effect of parallax on measurements

Figure 4.2a shows how parallax can lead to a rod appearing to be longer than its real length. Clearly, it is important to minimize the effects of parallax in measurements.

- From your observations of parallax effects, what can you deduce about the best location of a ruler, or any measuring scale, relative to an object whose position you want to measure?

❍ You should have observed that parallax was reduced when the ruler was brought closer to the book. So object and ruler should be as close together as possible — and ideally in the same plane — if parallax effects are to be minimized. ■

It is not always practical to position the object and scale in the same plane. When there is a separation between object and scale, the effect of parallax can be reduced in the ways shown in Figures 4.2b and c

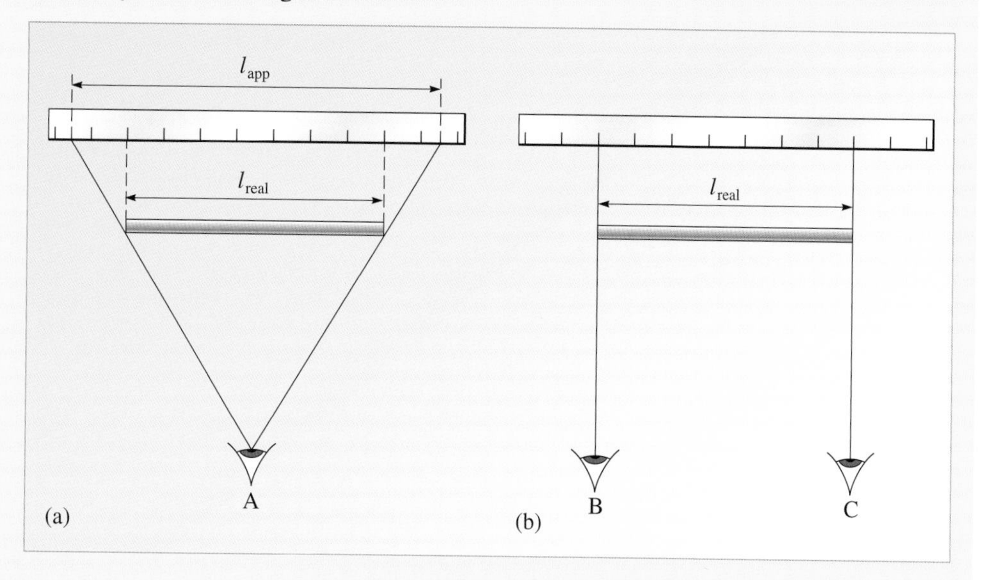

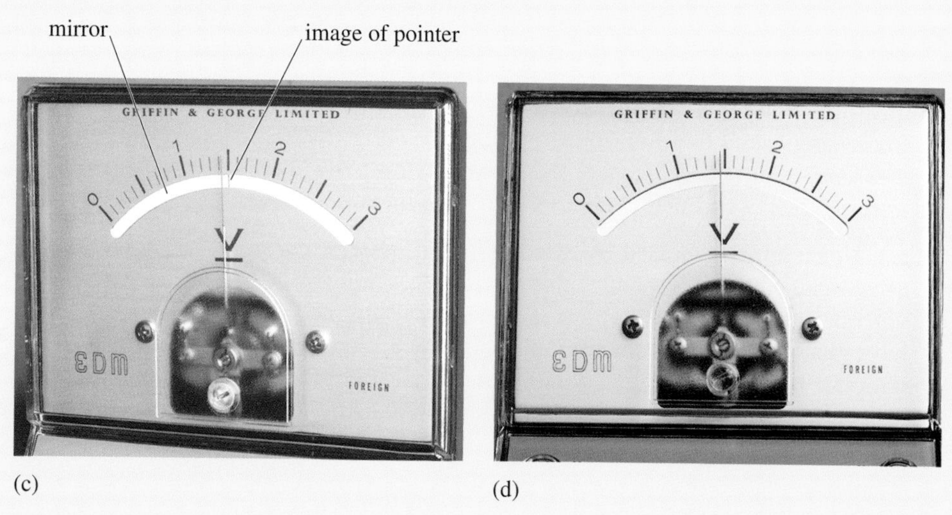

Figure 4.2 (a) If the positions of the ends of the object are noted with the eye in position A, then the apparent length is l_{app}. This is longer than the real length l_{real}, which would be measured if the ruler was placed in contact with the object. (b) If the ruler cannot be placed in contact with the object, then the parallax uncertainty can be minimized by noting the scale position of one end of the object when the eye is at B and of the other end when the eye is at C. (c) Getting the eye in the correct position to minimize parallax can be facilitated by using a mirror to ensure that the reading is taken from a direction perpendicular to the scale. When the eye is not in the correct position, the pointer of the voltmeter and its mirror image do not coincide (as shown here), and the apparent position of the pointer on the scale gives an incorrect reading, 1.41 V. (d) Moving the eye so that the pointer and its mirror image coincide ensures that the scale is read from directly in front of it, and in this case the pointer reading is 1.45 V.

(b) Instrumental limitations All measuring instruments have their limitations. Some are obvious, as in the case of cheap wooden rulers, where you may be able to see that the divisions are not equally spaced. Others are not so apparent: a metre rule may have equally-spaced divisions, but comparison with a more accurate rule may show that its length is 1002 mm rather than 1000 mm, so that all measurements are 0.2% too short. Even the most expensive and sophisticated instrument will have some limitation on its accuracy, and this is generally specified by its manufacturer. For example, the specification may indicate that the accuracy is ±0.5% of the reading, or possibly ±0.5% of full scale for the measuring range that is being used. The manufacturer may also say that the specified accuracy will only be obtained under certain conditions: for example, if a metal ruler is calibrated at 20 °C, it becomes less accurate as the temperature deviates from 20 °C, owing to the expansion or contraction of the metal. Uncertainties can also arise from imperfections in instruments: for example, friction in the mechanism of a balance may lead to uncertainties in measurements of mass.

(c) Uncertainties in taking measurements from a scale However well an instrument is calibrated, there will be uncertainties associated with the experimenter 'reading' a value for a measurement from the scale. With a digital instrument, the uncertainty will be determined by the discrete differences between successive values of the final digit displayed. For a measuring instrument with a graduated scale (such as a ruler, a mercury in glass thermometer or an analog voltmeter) the uncertainty will be determined partly by the fineness of the scale divisions, and partly by how well the observer can interpolate between scale divisions.

(d) Uncertainties caused by the act of measurement itself Connecting a pressure gauge to a tyre causes a small drop in the pressure, and this means that the measured pressure is slightly lower than the pressure before the measurement. Immersing a cold thermometer in a hot liquid cools the liquid slightly, so the measured temperature is lower than it was before. You should always watch out for uncertainties of this nature, and try to reduce them if you can.

(e) Uncertainties caused by extraneous influences A variety of unwanted effects can cause uncertainties in experiments. Draughts can lead to uncertainties when weighing an object with a balance, and so high-precision balances usually have glass cases around them to minimize the effects of draughts. Changes of temperature can lead to uncertainties in many experiments: for example, the resistances of many electronic components depend on temperature, and so changes in the ambient temperature can cause changes in the current through a component when a voltage difference is applied. Again, you should attempt to eliminate such effects, or at least reduce them.

All of the uncertainties that have been mentioned so far have their origin in the measuring instruments or the measuring process. They could be present even if the quantity being measured had a precisely defined and unchanging value. But there are other rather different uncertainties — uncertainties that could be present even if it were possible to devise an ideal measuring instrument capable of infinite precision. These other uncertainties are caused by variations in what is actually being measured. Here are a couple of examples.

(f) Uncertainties caused by real variations in the quantity that is measured In many physics experiments, the quantity that is being measured does not have a definite value. For example, in an experiment to determine the viscosity of a liquid by measuring the time taken for ball-bearings to fall a given distance through the liquid, an experimenter measures the diameters of a sample of the balls with a micrometer screw gauge (Box 4.2). Since the balls are not identical, there will be a spread in the values of the diameter, and this spread allows the experimenter to specify the uncertainty in the diameter of these ball-bearings. This uncertainty is due to variations in diameter within the population of ball-bearings, analogous to variations in the heights of six-year-old children in a school, say.

However, the balls may not be perfectly spherical, so that if you repeated measurements of the diameter of any one ball, making each measurement in a different direction, then you might end up with a spread of values. As long as this spread was too large to attribute to instrumental limitations or limitations on reading the scale, then the spread would indicate the extent to which the ball deviates from being perfectly spherical.

(g) Uncertainties caused by random fluctuations This is really a subdivision of the previous category, and involves (random) variations with time of the quantity being measured. The best example is radioactive decay of unstable atomic nuclei, which is a random process. If you use a Geiger counter to make a series of measurements of the number of decay events in, say, a minute, then you will record a spread of values. This spread is a measure of the inherent uncertainty in the number of decays per minute and this uncertainty is due to the randomness of the decay process.

There are other types of random fluctuations that lead to uncertainties in measurements. An important and ubiquitous example is the random voltage fluctuations in any electrical circuit due to fluctuations in the thermal motion of the conduction electrons. These fluctuations are commonly referred to as *noise*, and they are always present, superimposed on the voltage signal that is of interest.

Box 4.2 Micrometer screw gauge and vernier callipers

Scientists and engineers frequently need to measure dimensions of objects more precisely than is possible with a ruler. One instrument that has been devised for this purpose is the micrometer screw gauge, shown in Figure 4.3a, which can be used to measure the length or diameter of objects to ±0.002 mm. The movable jaw of the micrometer is screwed in until the object to be measured is gently held between the two jaws. A ratchet drive allows a small reproducible force to be applied to the object for each measurement.

The separation of the jaws, i.e. the diameter of the ball in Figure 4.3a, is read from the linear scale, which is graduated in 0.5 mm divisions, and from the rotating circular scale which is graduated in 0.01 mm divisions. One full turn of the circular scale corresponds to a 0.5 mm movement on the linear scale. The rim of the circular scale in Figure 4.3a lies between the 6 mm and 6.5 mm graduations, so the diameter of the ball is 6.xx mm. The tenths and hundredths of a millimetre are read from the point where the linear scale intersects the circular scale, and in the example shown the reading is 33.0, i.e. 0.330 mm. So the ball's diameter is 6.330 mm.

The combination of two scales used in the micrometer screw gauge is an example of a vernier scale, named after the French mathematician Pierre Vernier, who invented this type of scale in the seventeenth century. A more common form of vernier uses two adjacent linear scales, and this is the arrangement used in the vernier callipers shown in Figure 4.3b. The object to be measured is held between a fixed jaw and a movable jaw. Along the bottom edge of the shaft of the callipers is a scale graduated in millimetres, with the values 0, 10, 20, 30, … marked. Ignore the top scale of the shaft which is graduated in fractions of inches. The scale that is attached to the movable jaw has divisions labelled 0, 1, 2, … 10, and these are used to read off tenths of a millimetre. The subdivisions each correspond to 0.02 mm.

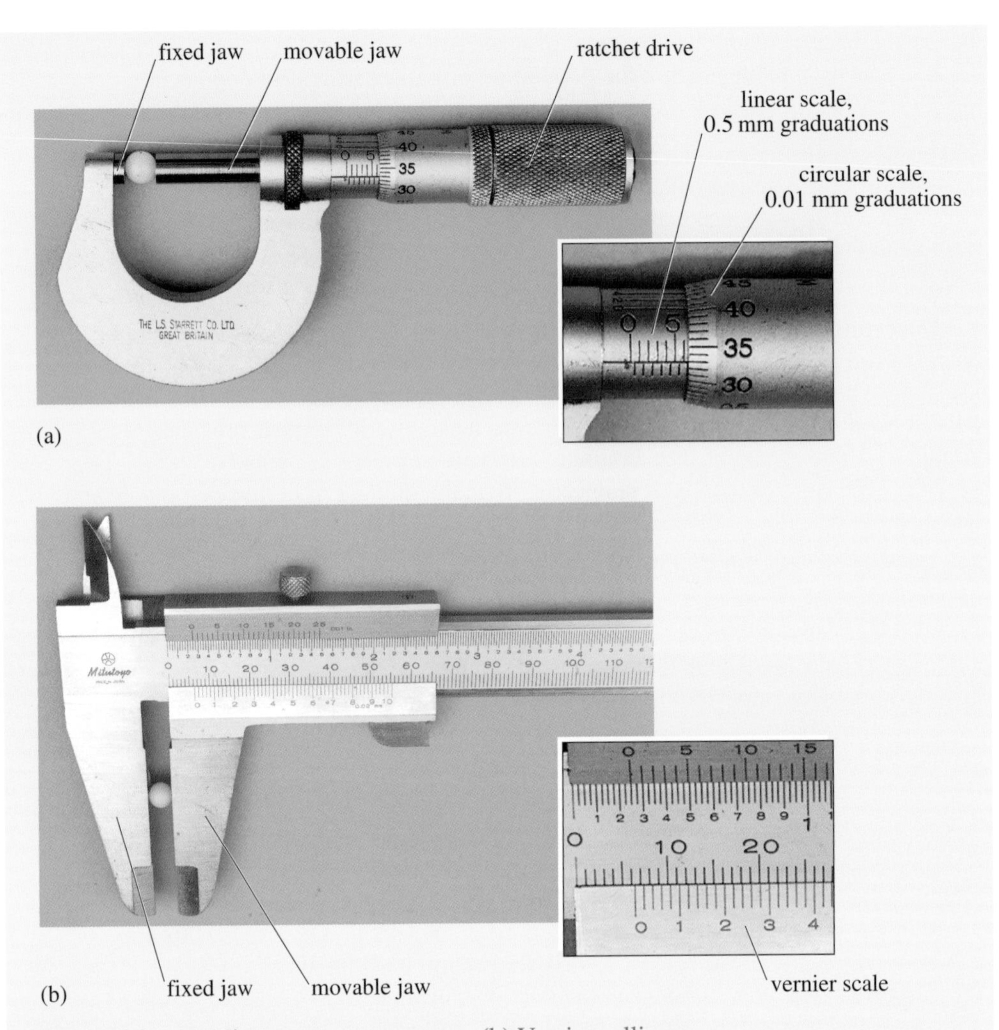

Figure 4.3 (a) Micrometer screw gauge. (b) Vernier callipers.

To read the diameter of the ball in Figure 4.3b, you should first note the position on the shaft scale of the zero line of the movable scale. In this case, the zero line is between 6 mm and 7 mm, so the diameter is '6 point something millimetres'. You can read the number of tenths of a millimetre from the movable scale. To do this, you look for the graduation on the movable scale that is most closely aligned with a graduation on the shaft scale. This requires good eyesight, or use of a magnifying lens; in this case the graduation corresponding to 3.4 on the movable scale appears to be the one that is best aligned. So the diameter is 3.4 tenths of a millimetre over 6 mm, which means that the diameter is 6.34 mm. The vernier callipers shown in Figure 4.3b can be read to the nearest 0.02 mm.

How does this type of vernier scale work? If you look carefully at the movable scale you will see that the distance between 0 and 10 on the movable scale corresponds to 49 mm on the shaft scale. This means that each of the 50 subdivisions corresponds to (49/50) mm = 0.98 mm. So if the zero of the movable scale is at 6.34 mm on the shaft scale, then the first subdivision of the movable scale will be at 6.34 + 0.98 = 7.32 on the shaft scale, the second will be at 6.34 + (2 × 0.98) = 8.30, the tenth at 6.34 + (10 × 0.98) = 16.14, and the seventeenth at 6.34 + (17 × 0.98) = 23.00. Thus the seventeenth subdivision — corresponding to 3.4 on the movable scale — aligns with the 23 mm graduation on the shaft scale. This indicates that the diameter is 17×0.02 mm = 0.34 mm over 6 mm, so the scale reading of 3.4 corresponds to the number of tenths of a millimetre.

Vernier scales with 10 subdivisions on the movable scale are very common. These allow you to read to one-tenth of a division of the main scale, compared to one-fiftieth of a division with the vernier in Figure 4.3b, which has 50 subdivisions.

4.2 Random and systematic uncertainties

The uncertainties that were described in Section 4.1 can be divided into two quite different types, those that are *random* and those that are said to be *systematic*.

A **random uncertainty** leads to measured values that are scattered in a random fashion over a limited range, as shown in Figure 4.4. The smaller the random uncertainty in the measurements, the smaller is the range over which they are scattered. Measurements for which the random uncertainty is small are described as **precise**.

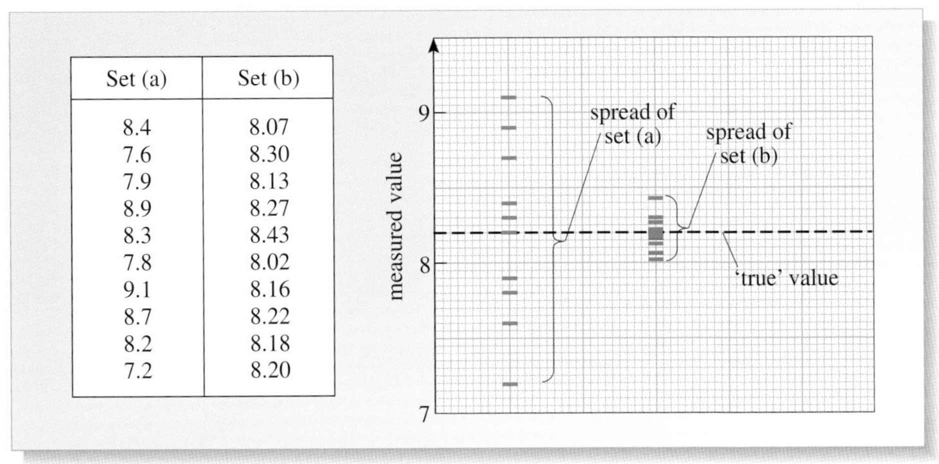

Set (a)	Set (b)
8.4	8.07
7.6	8.30
7.9	8.13
8.9	8.27
8.3	8.43
7.8	8.02
9.1	8.16
8.7	8.22
8.2	8.18
7.2	8.20

Figure 4.4 Two examples of random uncertainties. The two sets of measurements in the table, (a) and (b), are represented by the vertical positions of the dashes on the graph. The ten measured values for each set are scattered around the same 'true' value. However, the range over which the measurements are scattered is much larger for set (a) than for set (b). This indicates that the random uncertainty is greater for set (a) than for set (b), which means that the precision of the measurements is lower for set (a) than for set (b).

The best estimate that we can make for the value of the measured quantity is the mean, or average, of the measured values. As you might expect, if we make more measurements, then the mean value that we calculate is likely to be a better estimate of the quantity that we are measuring. We will make this statement quantitative in Section 6.1.

Systematic uncertainties have a different effect on measurements. A **systematic uncertainty** leads to measured values that are all displaced in a similar way from the 'true' value, and this is illustrated in Figure 4.5. The two examples shown have the same random uncertainty — in both cases the spread, or scatter, of the values is the same. However, in both cases the measured values are systematically displaced from the 'true' value. The values in set (a) are all smaller than the 'true' value, and the values in set (b) are all larger. The difference between the mean value of a set of measurements and the 'true' value is the systematic uncertainty. Measurements in which the systematic uncertainty is small are described as **accurate**. Therefore, to improve the accuracy of a measurement we need to reduce the systematic uncertainties.

The problem for experimenters is that they don't generally know the 'true' value, otherwise they would not need to make the measurement. So they need to estimate the possible magnitudes of systematic uncertainties by considering details of the apparatus and experimental procedures. Alternatively, they need to devise a method of eliminating the systematic uncertainties: for example, the effect of a (systematic) uncertainty in the zero reading of an electrical instrument can often be eliminated by reversing the electric current, and averaging the measurements obtained for the two current directions.

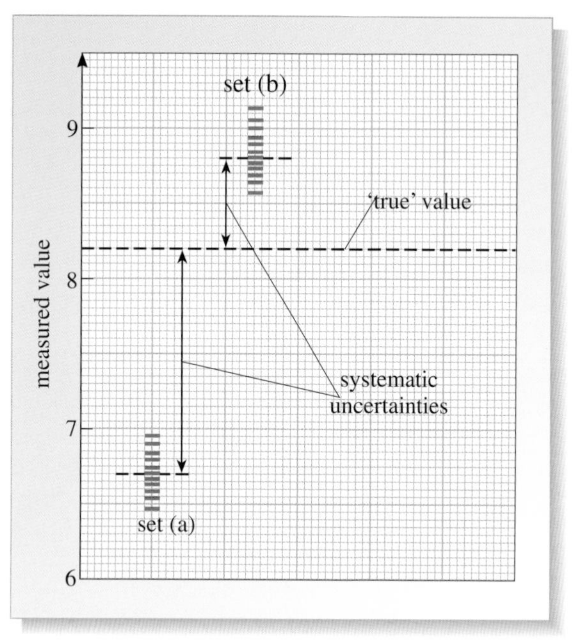

Figure 4.5 The effect of systematic uncertainties. Two sets of measurements, (a) and (b), are represented by the vertical positions of the dashes on the graph. For set (a), the systematic uncertainty causes all of the measured values to be smaller than the 'true' value. For set (b) the systematic uncertainty causes all of the values to be larger than the 'true' value, but the magnitude of the uncertainty is smaller than for set (a). The measurements in set (b) are therefore more accurate than those in set (a).

Now you might conclude that the goal of every experimental physicist is to ensure that their measurements are as *precise* as possible (i.e. smallest possible *random* uncertainties) and as *accurate* as possible (i.e. smallest possible *systematic* uncertainties). However, life is not that simple. Compromises always have to be made. How much time do you have to make the measurements? What measuring instruments are available, or what can you afford to buy? What is the purpose of the experiment? (After all, there is no point in trying to obtain a result that has a precision of ±0.01% if ±1% would be sufficient.) In addition, you may want to make a trade-off between accuracy and precision. Before these decisions can be made, you need to be able to estimate the accuracy and precision of measurements, or in other words, you need to be able to estimate the magnitudes of the systematic and random uncertainties. We will discuss various ways of doing this in the next section.

Question 4.1 The acceleration due to gravity g can be determined by measuring the time period T of a simple pendulum of length l, and then using the relationship

$$T = 2\pi\sqrt{\frac{l}{g}}.$$

A student times the swings of a bunch of keys attached to the end of a piece of string, about 2 m long, attached to a hook in the ceiling. The length l of the pendulum is measured with a wooden metre rule, and the timing is done with a digital stopwatch. (a) List the uncertainties that may be present in this experiment. (b) Which of these uncertainties are likely to be random, and which systematic? ■

5 Estimating uncertainties

One of the most difficult aspects of an experiment can be the estimation of the uncertainties in the measurements. No two experiments are identical, so there are no definite rules about how you estimate the magnitude of the uncertainties. However, it is very largely a matter of common sense. We will provide a few examples that illustrate how uncertainties can be quantified, and these should help you to decide how to approach estimating the uncertainties in experiments that you do.

In many experiments, more than one of the types of uncertainty discussed in Section 4.1 will affect a measurement. Sometimes you will be able to estimate the magnitude of each of the uncertainties individually and sometimes you will only be able to estimate their combined effect. But you should always keep in mind that it is only an *estimate* of the uncertainty that is required. By definition, an uncertainty cannot have an exact value, and it is generally sufficient to estimate the value of an uncertainty to one significant figure, or perhaps two. The uncertainty then allows you to decide how many significant figures to quote in a result. For example, if the result of a calculation is that $g = 9.831\,467\ldots\ \mathrm{m\,s^{-2}}$, and the uncertainty is calculated to be $0.032\,648\ \mathrm{m\,s^{-2}}$, then you should quote the result as $(9.83 \pm 0.03)\ \mathrm{m\,s^{-2}}$. Here the uncertainty is rounded to one significant figure, and the best value is rounded to three significant figures, since then the uncertainty is affecting the last digit.

Zeroes at the *start* of a number are *not* significant figures. Thus 0.0023 has two significant figures, but 1.0023 has five significant figures.

5.1 Estimating random uncertainties

We will start by considering random uncertainties, because they are often more straightforward to estimate than systematic uncertainties. Let's consider a specific experiment in which the viscosity of water is determined by measuring the rate at which water flows through a small-diameter tube in response to an applied pressure difference between the ends of the tube. Suppose that we collected the water for 4 minutes, and measured its volume as $436.5\ \mathrm{cm^3}$. What random uncertainty would we associate with such a measurement? Is it $\pm 0.1\ \mathrm{cm^3}$, $\pm 0.5\ \mathrm{cm^3}$, or perhaps $\pm 1\ \mathrm{cm^3}$?

There are two distinct methods of estimating random uncertainties: one method involves repeating the measurement a number of times, and the other involves estimating the uncertainty from knowledge about the instruments and techniques involved and about the skill of the experimenter. It is good practice to use both methods and to check that they produce consistent estimates, but this will not always be feasible.

Estimating random uncertainties by repeating measurements

One way to estimate the magnitude of random uncertainties in a measured value is by making a series of repeated measurements of the quantity. Random uncertainties lead to a scatter in measured values, and the uncertainty in the measurements can be deduced from the range over which the values are scattered. So for the viscosity experiment, introduced at the start of this section, we could make a series of, say, five measurements of the volume of water flowing through the tube in 4 minutes.

Suppose that the results were:

$$436.5\,\text{cm}^3 \quad 437.5\,\text{cm}^3 \quad 435.9\,\text{cm}^3 \quad 436.2\,\text{cm}^3 \quad 436.9\,\text{cm}^3\,.$$

Let us assume that these measurements were all made with the same care and skill, and with the same measuring instruments. Then the best estimate we can make of the water volume is the mean value of the five measurements.

The **mean** of a set of n measurements $x_1, x_2, x_3, \ldots, x_n$ is denoted by $\langle x \rangle$ and is defined as:

$$\langle x \rangle = \frac{x_1 + x_2 + x_3 + \ldots + x_n}{n} = \frac{1}{n}\sum_{i=1}^{n} x_i. \tag{5.1}$$

The mean $\langle V \rangle$ for the water volume measurements is given by:

$$\langle V \rangle = \frac{(436.5 + 437.5 + 435.9 + 436.2 + 436.9)\,\text{cm}^3}{5}$$

$$= 436.6\,\text{cm}^3.$$

Now if there had been no random uncertainty associated with the measurement of the volume, then all of the five values would have been identical. The effect of the random uncertainty is to scatter the measurements around the 'true' value, and the larger the random uncertainty, the greater will be the range over which the measurements will be scattered, i.e. the lower will be the precision of the measurements. The extent of the scatter therefore indicates:

- the magnitude of the random uncertainty;
- how far from the 'true' value a typical measurement is likely to be;
- conversely, how far from a measured value the 'true' value might be;
- the precision of the measurement.

The five water flow measurements are scattered between $435.9\,\text{cm}^3$ and $437.5\,\text{cm}^3$, which is a range of $1.6\,\text{cm}^3$, or a spread of about $\pm 0.8\,\text{cm}^3$ around the mean. This spread of $\pm 0.8\,\text{cm}^3$ is one way of quantifying the random uncertainty of the measurements, and we would expect that additional measurements would lie roughly within this range.

However, this is a somewhat pessimistic estimate of the uncertainty in a typical measurement, because more of the measurements will lie in the centre of the range than lie at either extreme of the range. So, as a rough rule of thumb, we generally take the uncertainty in each measurement as about 2/3 of the spread of the values. In the example above, we would quote the uncertainty as $2/3 \times (\pm 0.8\,\text{cm}^3) = \pm 0.5\,\text{cm}^3$. This simple procedure is perfectly adequate in many cases, particularly when a relatively small number of measurements is involved.

So for the water flow measurement we could say that:

- the magnitude of the random uncertainty is $\pm 0.5\,\text{cm}^3$;
- a typical measurement is likely to be within $\pm 0.5\,\text{cm}^3$ of the true value;
- conversely, the 'true' value is likely to be within $\pm 0.5\,\text{cm}^3$ of a measured value;
- the precision of the measurement is $\pm 0.5\,\text{cm}^3$.

Obviously if one measurement were very different from all the others, then using the spread to determine the uncertainty would give a misleadingly pessimistic value.

Common sense suggests that a single deviant reading should be ignored when estimating the mean and the uncertainty, and suggests that a few more measurements should be taken. For example, if the last reading for the volume were 432.9 cm^3 rather than 436.9 cm^3, then it would be wise to ignore it.

In the water-flow example, the variability in the measured values of V could arise not only from real variations in the rate at which the water flows through the tube, but also from uncertainties in the measuring process used. Even if it were possible to make exact measurements of the volume collected in 4 minutes (i.e. we had a 'perfect' measurement technique), there would be variability in the measured values if the flow rate were varying — possibly due to changes in the water pressure or the temperature. And even if the 'true' flow rate did not vary, then there could be variability in the measured values because of uncertainties in the measuring process, for example, uncertainties in timing the four-minute collecting period; inserting and removing the beaker to collect the water too early or too late; uncertainties in reading the volume scale. However, by repeating the measurements we get an overall measure of the random uncertainties, and it isn't necessary to make separate assessments of the random uncertainties due to these different factors.

So, generally, you should not be satisfied with making a single measurement of a quantity, but should repeat the measurement several times. Whenever possible, it is good practice to reset the measuring instrument between successive measurements. For example, if you were measuring the length of a rod, you should remove the ruler, and reposition it, before reading the length again. You would then have to interpolate between different scale marks on the ruler. If you were measuring the diameter of a wire with a screw-gauge, then you should remove the gauge and reposition it to a different point on the circumference of the wire before taking another measurement. You might then reposition it to a different point along the wire for the next measurement, and so on. As a third example, if you were using a travelling microscope to measure the position of an interference fringe in a photograph, then you would reset the crosshairs of the microscope at the (fuzzy) centre of the fringe's image a number of times in order to determine a mean value of its position.

So here is an important point that is worth emphasizing:

> The presence of a random uncertainty in a measurement can be detected, and its magnitude estimated, by repeating the measurement a number of times.

Repeating measurements is particularly important when measuring a quantity that has an in-built variability. You might want to know the mean diameter and the uncertainty in the diameter of a batch of ball-bearings. If you wanted to get reliable estimates, then you would have to make sure that (i) you took sufficient measurements, and (ii) the measurements were a representative sample. Five to ten measurements of ball diameter would probably be sufficient. Picking balls at random from a large number tipped into a dish should give a representative sample.

Estimating random uncertainties from information about the instruments and techniques used

The second method of estimating random uncertainties only applies to uncertainties arising from the measuring process, and doesn't tell you anything about any variability in the quantity that is being measured. The method is particularly important when it is not possible to repeat measurements. It requires the experimenter to use their knowledge of, and experience with, the measuring instruments and the experimental techniques to estimate the likely random uncertainties.

Suppose that you do an experiment that involves heating a liquid and measuring its temperature at different times with a mercury-in-glass thermometer. Since the temperature is changing, it is not possible to repeat measurements. If the thermometer had a scale like the one shown in Figure 5.1a, then you might judge that you could interpolate to about 1/4 of a division, i.e. the nearest 1/2 of a degree. In favourable circumstances — good lighting, good eyesight, sufficient space between the graduations — you may be able to do better and read the scale to 1/10 of a division. Of course, if the conditions were not so favourable, you may think that you can only interpolate to one-half of a division (1 °C).

Clearly, if the experimenter always recorded the temperature from the thermometer shown in Figure 5.1a to the nearest division, they would be losing some precision. It is always worth trying to interpolate between divisions on a scale as precisely as you can, and this may mean recording a value to the nearest one-tenth of a division even though you quote an uncertainty of ±0.2 divisions or more.

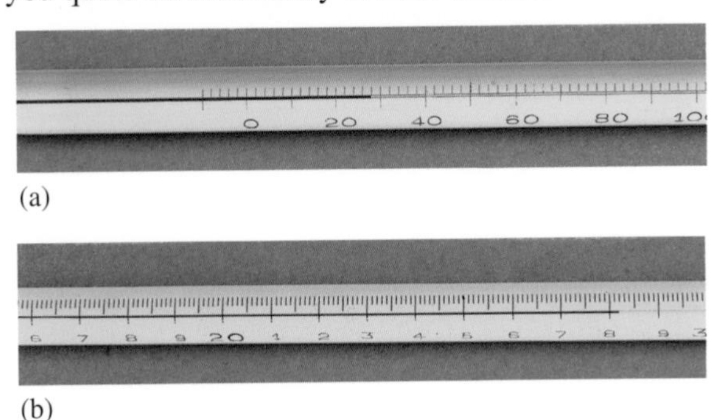

Figure 5.1 The temperature scale in (a) can probably be read to the nearest 0.5 °C, and the scale in (b) to the nearest 0.05 °C.

However, suppose that you measured the temperature with a thermometer with the more expanded scale shown in Figure 5.1b. This scale can be read more precisely: a value of 28.20 °C could be recorded in this case if the scale can be read to the nearest 1/2 of a division, 0.05 °C. If repeated measurements all gave the result 28.20 °C, then you would have to conclude that the uncertainty was ±0.05 °C, with the precision limited by your ability to read the scale to one-half of a division. Of course, with the better scale, repeated measurement might show some variability, and this would indicate that the uncertainty was greater than ±0.05 °C.

With a digital instrument, the best possible precision of a reading is ±1/2 of the least significant digit. Therefore, if a digital meter displays 1.734 V, then the best we can say is that the measured voltage is 1.734 V ± 0.0005 V. However, in practice, the uncertainty would be greater than ±0.0005 V, because there would be calibration uncertainties to consider too.

Returning to the water-flow measurement, suppose that we had only made one measurement of the volume of water collected in 4 minutes. We could then make estimates of some of the random uncertainties that might contribute to the overall uncertainty in the volume. For example, we might estimate that there could be a random uncertainty of ±0.2 cm^3 in reading the scale on the measuring cylinder used to measure water volume. In addition, we might estimate that there could be an uncertainty of ±0.5 s in the 4-minute collection period, due to the measuring cylinder not being inserted/removed from the flow exactly at the start/end of the period.

However, as well as the uncertainties that are associated with the measuring instruments and procedures, there could also be a random uncertainty due to variations in the flow rate. It isn't possible to estimate this without more information. Separate experiments would need to be done to investigate how the flow rate depended on pressure head and temperature, and estimates would then be needed of the possible variations in pressure and temperature. You can see that this approach can become quite complex and time consuming, and this underlines our advice that random uncertainties are often best estimated by repeating measurements.

Estimating uncertainties when measurements are reproducible

One fairly common situation in which you will need to make use of information about the measuring instrument to estimate the uncertainties is when you repeat an experimental measurement, and you record exactly the same result each time. For example, if you measured the temperature of an object five times, your results might be:

73 °C 73 °C 73 °C 73 °C 73 °C

i.e. five identical readings. However, the reproducibility of the measurements does not mean that there is no uncertainty in this temperature of 73 °C.

If you write down 73 °C for each measurement, you are implicitly indicating that you measured the temperature to the nearest degree. You thought that the temperature was closer to 73 °C than it was to 72 °C or to 74 °C, so the temperature was likely to have been between 72.5 °C and 73.5 °C. The uncertainty is therefore ±0.5 °C, and the temperature should be quoted as (73 ± 0.5) °C. The uncertainty of ±0.5 °C may be a consequence of the limitations of the thermometer and/or your inability (or unwillingness) to read the scale to higher precision. So when using any measuring instrument, you need to assess its inherent limitations.

Question 5.1 (a) What is the width in centimetres of the metal strip shown in Figure 5.2a? (The upper scale is graduated in centimetres and millimetres.)

(b) What is the temperature indicated by the thermometer in Figure 5.2b? (The thermometer is graduated in °C.)

(c) What is the voltage reading on the voltmeter shown in Figure 5.2c?

(d) What is the diameter in millimetres of the coin in Figure 5.2d? (The lower scale is graduated in millimetres. Box 4.2 indicates how a vernier scale is read.) ■

(a)

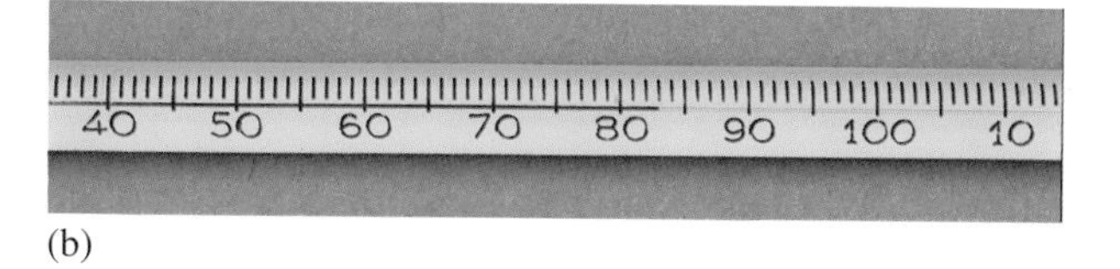

(b)

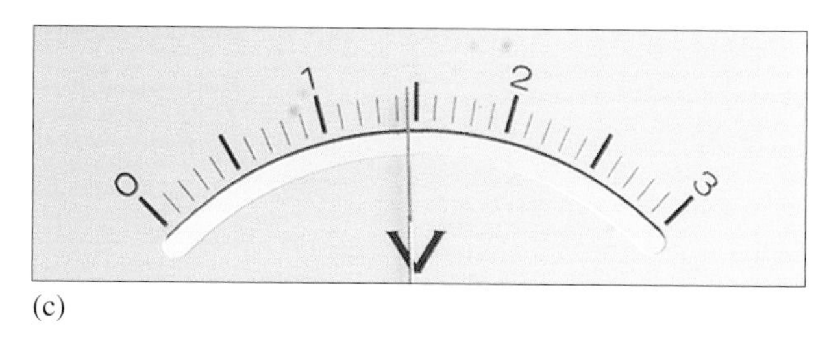

(c)

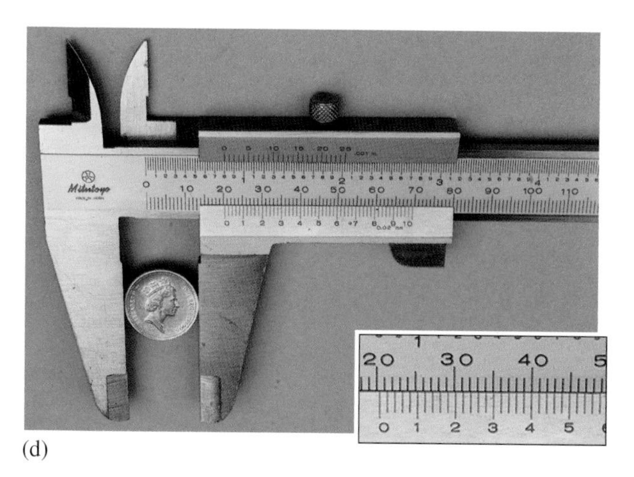

(d)

Figure 5.2 (a) A ruler being used to measure the width of a metal strip. (b) A mercury-in-glass thermometer. (c) A voltmeter. (d) Vernier callipers being used to measure the diameter of a coin.

5.2 The distribution of measurements with random uncertainties

When discussing repeated measurements, we have been concerned with small numbers of measurements, and have characterized the scatter of the values of the measured quantity by 2/3 of the spread of the values. As more measurements are made, they are likely to be scattered over approximately the same range, i.e. the spread will remain the same. However, the measured values are not evenly scattered throughout this range.

Let's consider a hypothetical experiment that involves measuring the force required to break copper wire of a certain diameter, and look at the distribution of a set of measurements. Figure 5.3a shows a histogram of the distribution of 10 measurements of force, where the height of each bar on the histogram represents the number of measurements within a certain 0.1 N interval of force. So, for example, the tallest bar indicates that four of the measurements were between 12.5 N and 12.6 N. The spread of the results is 0.6 N, or ±0.3 N, so we would say that the uncertainty in a single measurement was about ±0.2 N.

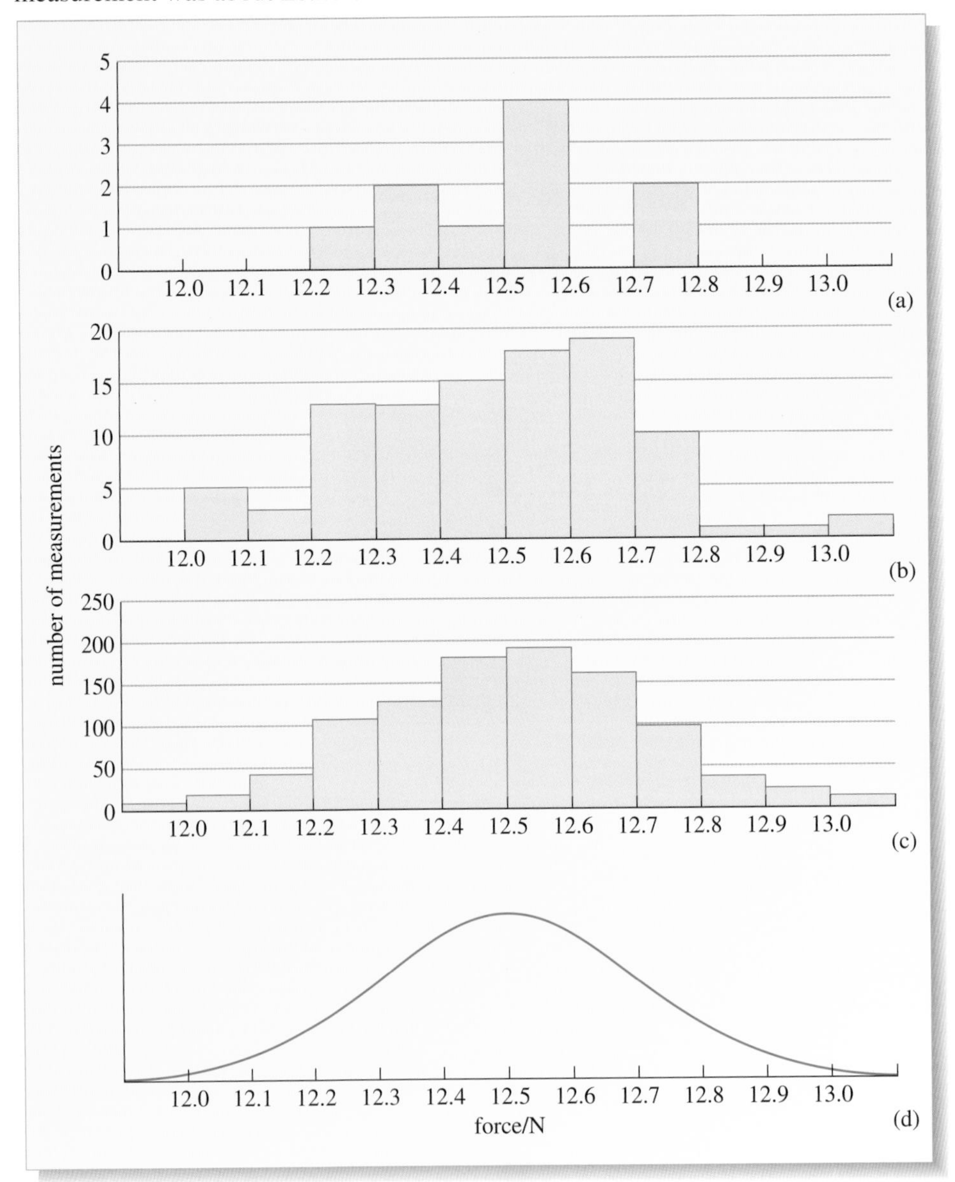

Figure 5.3 Histograms showing the distribution of measurements of the force used to break a thin copper wire for (a) 10 measurements, (b) 100 measurements, (c) 1000 measurements. (d) The smooth curve that represents the distribution of a very large number of measurements separated into very small intervals of force.

Figure 5.3b shows a distribution of 100 measurements. There is a smoother variation of the heights of the bars, and the overall spread of the distribution is somewhat larger than that for 10 measurements. Now imagine that we make 1000 measurements, as shown in Figure 5.3c. The distribution is beginning to take on a bell shape. Continuing this process to the limit of a very large number of measurements with very small intervals of force, the envelope of the histogram bars would tend to become a smooth bell-shaped curve (Figure 5.3d).

The spread of the distribution

The distributions in Figure 5.3b–d all have extended wings on either side of the central peak. This means that using the overall spread of the measurements, or even 2/3 of the overall spread, as a measure of the random uncertainty may give a misleading estimate of how far a typical measurement lies from the mean, since the spread is determined by only the maximum and minimum values. To avoid this problem, we need a measure of the random uncertainty that depends on the values of all of the measurements, not just the extreme two. The quantity that is widely used for this purpose is the *standard deviation* of the measurements, and Box 5.1 shows an example of how the standard deviation is calculated.

The process of calculating the standard deviation described in Box 5.1 is an extended definition, but it is useful to have a more succinct definition.

The **standard deviation** s of a set of n measured values x_i is the square root of the mean of the squares of the deviations d_i of the measured values from their mean value $\langle x \rangle$.

$$s = \sqrt{\langle d_i^2 \rangle} = \sqrt{\frac{1}{n}\sum_{i=1}^{n} d_i^2} \qquad (5.5)$$

where the deviation d_i of the measured value x_i from the mean value $\langle x \rangle$ is

$$d_i = x_i - \langle x \rangle, \qquad (5.3)$$

and the mean value $\langle x \rangle$ of the measurements is

$$\langle x \rangle = \frac{x_1 + x_2 + x_3 + \ldots + x_n}{n} = \frac{1}{n}\sum_{i=1}^{n} x_i. \qquad (5.1)$$

The standard deviation is the most commonly used measure of the scatter of a set of measurements, and is used to quantify the likely random uncertainty in a single measurement.

How do values for the standard deviation compare with what we would get by using the simple '2/3 spread' rule introduced earlier? Well, for the data in Table 5.1, the spread is 5.6 – 5.0 = 0.6, or ±0.3, so 2/3 of the spread is ±0.2. The standard deviation calculated in Box 5.1 is 0.176, or 0.2 to one significant figure. This indicates why the simple rule is adequate for many situations where we only need a rough estimate of the uncertainty of a measurement.

Box 5.1 Calculating the standard deviation of a set of measurements

The six steps below describe how the standard deviation is calculated. Table 5.1 is an example of this calculation, and the bold numbers and letters on the table correspond to the numbered steps. As you read each step, you should refer to the corresponding part of the tabulated calculation.

1 Start with a set of measured values $x_1, x_2, x_3, \ldots x_n$. In the example in Table 5.1, $n = 8$.

2a Add together all of the values x_i.

2b Divide the sum by the number of values n to obtain the mean value $\langle x \rangle$ of the measurements:

$$\langle x \rangle = \frac{x_1 + x_2 + x_3 + \ldots + x_n}{n} = \frac{1}{n}\sum_{i=1}^{n} x_i. \tag{5.1}$$

3 The deviation d of a measurement x is defined as the difference between that measurement and the mean $\langle x \rangle$ of the set of measurements:

$$d = x - \langle x \rangle. \tag{5.2}$$

You should now calculate the deviations d_i corresponding to each value x_i:

$$d_i = x_i - \langle x \rangle. \tag{5.3}$$

4 Calculate the squares of each of the deviations, d_i^2.

5a Add together all of the squares of the deviations d_i^2.

5b Divide by the number of values n to obtain the mean square deviation:

$$\langle d_i^2 \rangle = \frac{1}{n}\sum_{i=1}^{n} d_i^2. \tag{5.4}$$

6 Take the square root of the mean square deviation. It is this 'root mean square deviation' that is known as the standard deviation s:

$$s = \sqrt{\langle d_i^2 \rangle} = \sqrt{\frac{1}{n}\sum_{i=1}^{n} d_i^2}. \tag{5.5}$$

The standard deviation is generally quoted to one or two significant figures.

Table 5.1 An example of how the standard deviation of a set of measurements is calculated.

1 Measured value, x_i	**3** Deviation, $d_i = x_i - \langle x \rangle$	**4** Square deviation, d_i^2
5.3	+0.01	0.0001
5.4	+0.11	0.0121
5.4	+0.11	0.0121
5.1	−0.19	0.0361
5.0	−0.29	0.0841
5.2	−0.09	0.0081
5.6	+0.31	0.0961
5.3	+0.01	0.0001
2a Sum of 8 values, $\Sigma x_i = 42.3$		**5a** Sum of square deviations, $\Sigma d_i^2 = 0.2488$
2b Mean of 8 values, $\Sigma x_i / n = \langle x \rangle = 5.29$		**5b** Mean of square deviations, $\langle d_i^2 \rangle = \Sigma d_i^2 / n = 0.0311$
		6 Square root of mean square deviation, $s = \sqrt{\langle d_i^2 \rangle} = 0.176$, or $s = 0.2$ to 1 sig. fig.

The shape of the distribution

In real physics experiments, as opposed to hypothetical ones, experimenters rarely make sufficient measurements to obtain a smooth distribution. Even if they did, the precise shape of the distribution curve might depend on the particular measurements that were being made. However, it is convenient to assume a standard mathematical form for the typical distribution of measurements, and the form that is widely used is the so-called *normal distribution*, which is also known as the Gaussian distribution. This is the distribution shown in Figure 5.3d.

Figure 5.4 shows how the standard deviation of a normal distribution curve is related to the spread of the curve. It is clear that a substantial fraction of measurements deviates from the mean value by more than the standard deviation s. For a particular range of the measured variable x, the area under the distribution curve represents the fraction of measurements that lie within that range. For a normal distribution, 68% of measurements lie within one standard deviation, i.e. within $\pm s$, of the mean value. Conversely, 32% of measurements are expected to differ from the mean by more than the standard deviation s. Note that the distribution curve falls off rapidly as the measurements deviate further from the mean. Table 5.2 shows the percentage of measurements falling within specified ranges centred on the mean value.

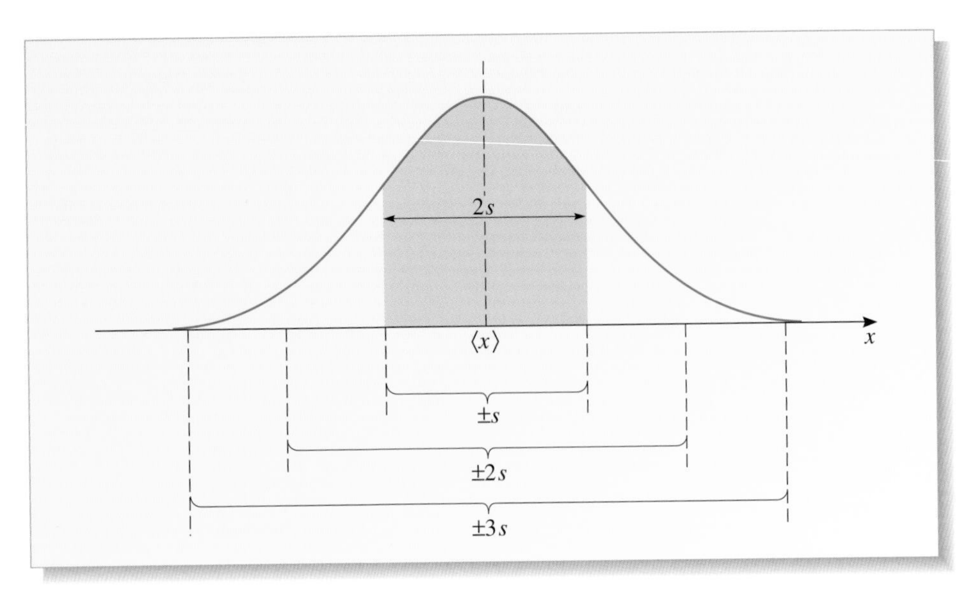

Figure 5.4 The standard deviation s characterizes the width of the normal distribution. The area shaded blue under this normal distribution curve represents the measurements that lie within $\pm s$ of the mean. This area is 68% of the total area under the curve, indicating that 68% of measurements are expected to fall within this range.

Table 5.2 The percentages of measurements within, and outside, various ranges of values centred on the mean for a normal distribution.

Range centred on mean value	$\pm s$	$\pm 2s$	$\pm 3s$	$\pm 4s$
Measurements within range	68%	95%	99.7%	99.994%
Measurements outside range	32%	5%	0.3%	0.006%

It is important to bear these percentages in mind when the standard deviation is used to indicate the uncertainty in a measurement. The statement that $x = 22.4\,\text{mm} \pm 0.4\,\text{mm}$ does not mean that all measurements of the quantity x will lie within the range from 22.0 mm to 22.8 mm. If the standard deviation is 0.4 mm, then on average only 68% of measurements will lie within a range of ±0.4 mm of the mean and 32% will lie outside. Therefore, the odds are roughly 2 to 1 that a measurement will lie within one standard deviation (i.e. within $\pm s$) of the mean.

The standard deviation is a measure of the precision of measurements. The greater the precision, the smaller will be the scatter and therefore the smaller will be the standard deviation. This means that the normal distribution curve will have a much narrower peak around the mean value $\langle x \rangle$, and this is illustrated by the three distribution curves shown in Figure 5.5.

Question 5.2 Ten measurements were made of the resistance R of an electrical component, and the values obtained in Ω were:

22.0, 21.6, 21.8, 22.3, 22.1, 22.0, 21.9, 22.2, 21.9, 22.2.

(a) What is the mean value of the resistance?

(b) Use the spread of the measurements to estimate the random uncertainty in an individual measurement of resistance.

(c) Calculate the standard deviation of the ten measurements, and compare it with the estimate of the random uncertainty obtained in part (b). ■

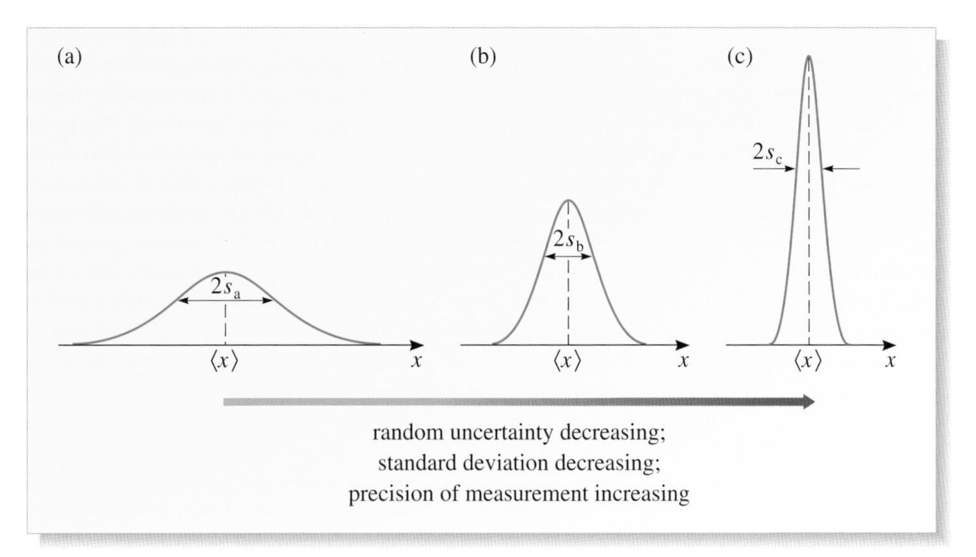

Figure 5.5 Normal distribution curves representing three large sets of measurements. The broadest and least highly peaked of the three curves (a) has the largest standard deviation, and corresponds to measurements with the largest random uncertainties and with the lowest precision. By contrast, (c) is the most highly peaked curve and corresponds to measurements with the highest precision. Curve (b) corresponds to measurements with precision between (a) and (c).

5.3 Uncertainties when counting randomly occurring events

An important type of random uncertainty arises when investigating processes that are inherently random, such as radioactive decay. In this section you will see that the magnitude of this type of uncertainty can easily be calculated using a simple expression.

Let's consider an experiment in which a Geiger counter is used to determine the number of nuclei decaying each minute in a pellet of material containing a very large number of unstable (radioactive) nuclei. Suppose that you counted 107 decays in one minute. How many decays would you observe if you repeated the measurement for another one-minute period?

Since each individual decay process is a random event, the number of decays in a period of one minute will vary. However, measurements of the number of decays each minute will be clustered around a well defined mean value $\langle n \rangle$. In fact, if you performed the experiment 1000 times you might find that measurements of the number of decays per minute were distributed as shown by the histogram in Figure 5.6a (overleaf).

The mean $\langle n \rangle$ of the 1000 measurements corresponds to the position of the centre of the peak of this symmetrical distribution, i.e. 100 decays per minute. If you were to calculate the value of the standard deviation from the results in the histogram you would get a value of 10 decays per minute. As you saw in Section 5.2, the standard deviation is used as a measure of the random uncertainty in a single measurement, and so we can say that the uncertainty in this case is ± 10. It is *not* a coincidence that this uncertainty of ± 10 is the same as the square root of the mean number of counts, 100.

Now imagine that you make many successive measurements of the number of randomly occurring events (such as radioactive decays) in a given period. As the number of measurements increases, the envelope of the histogram of the results will tend to a normal distribution curve, as shown in Figure 5.6b. The centre of the distribution indicates the mean number $\langle n \rangle$ of events in the given period. More interestingly in the present context, the standard deviation of the measurements is $\sqrt{\langle n \rangle}$, and so, as was shown in Figure 5.4, 68% of the measurements lie within

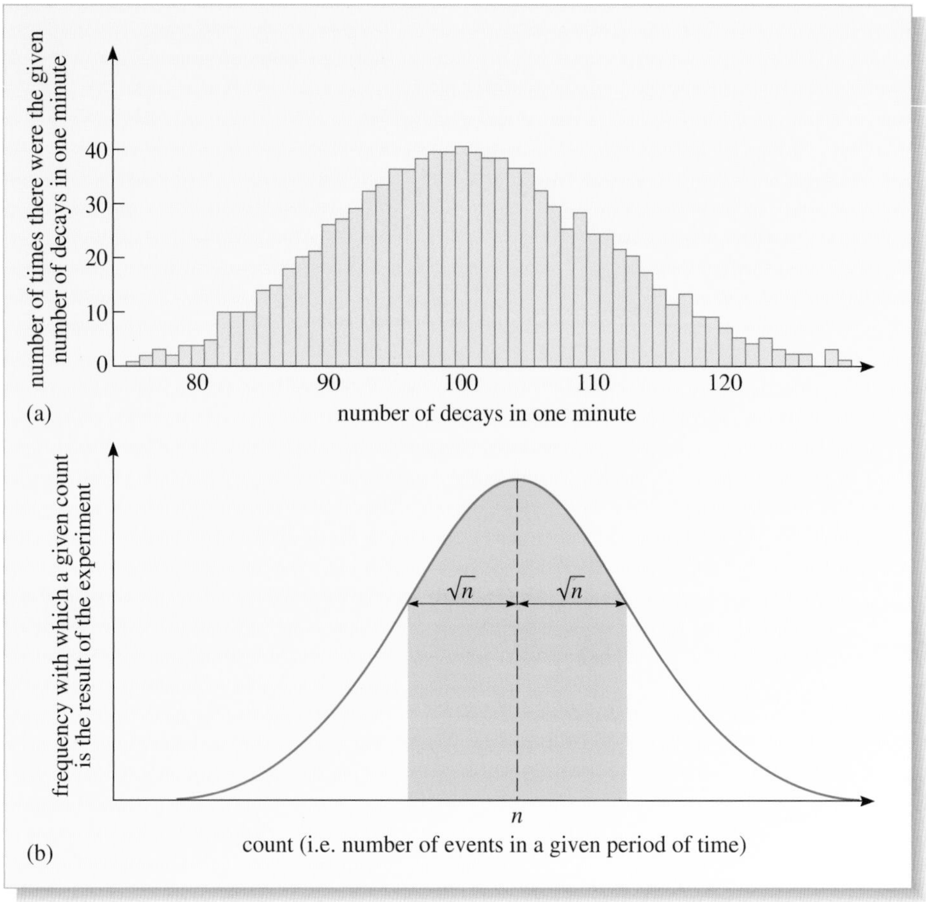

Figure 5.6 (a) A histogram showing how often particular numbers of radioactive decays were recorded in 1000 counting periods of 1 minute. (b) The distribution of the results from a very large number of identical experiments approximate to a normal distribution curve. The mean $\langle n \rangle$ corresponds to the centre of the peak and 68% of all the measurements are within $\pm\sqrt{n}$ of this mean.

$\pm\sqrt{\langle n \rangle}$ of the mean. For example, if the mean is 100 counts, then 68% of the measurements will produce a result between 90 and 110 counts. Alternatively, if the mean is 900 counts, 68% of the results will lie between 870 and 930. The standard deviation $\sqrt{\langle n \rangle}$ defines the width of the distribution, and it is therefore straightforward to identify the uncertainty associated with a single counting measurement.

If the number of *randomly occurring events* counted in a given period is n, the uncertainty in this number is given by:

$$\text{uncertainty} = \sqrt{n}\,. \qquad (5.6)$$

This uncertainty is a measure of the likely difference between the value n and the value of the mean that would be found from a long series of repeated measurements.

Now Equation 5.6 indicates that the uncertainty increases as the number of events counted increases. With the example we have used, about 100 events were counted in a one-minute period, and the uncertainty is about ±10. In a six-second period, only about 10 events would be counted, with an uncertainty of ±3. Increasing the counting period to 10 minutes would give about (1000 ± 32) counts, and 100 minutes would give about (10 000 ± 100) counts.

- Do these numbers suggest that it is better to count for a shorter period than for a longer period?

❍ No. It is true that the uncertainty in the number of counts gets smaller as the counting period gets shorter (and the number of counts gets smaller). However, the uncertainty $\sqrt{n}$ becomes a much larger *fraction* of the number of counts n as the counting period gets shorter. By counting for a longer time we can reduce the uncertainty $\sqrt{n}$ as a fraction of the number of counts n. ■

It is important to note that *increasing* the number of counts *reduces* the fractional uncertainty:

$$\text{fractional uncertainty} = \frac{\text{uncertainty}}{\text{measured value}} = \frac{\sqrt{n}}{n} = \frac{1}{\sqrt{n}}. \quad (5.7)$$

This reduction in the fractional uncertainty as the counting period (and hence the number of counts) increases is demonstrated by the data in Table 5.3.

Table 5.3 Uncertainties associated with counting random events for different periods, with the same mean count rate (100 counts per minute) in each case. Although the uncertainty *increases* as $\sqrt{n}$ (third row) as the counting period *increases*, the fractional uncertainty $\sqrt{n}/n$ (fourth row) *decreases*.

Counting period t/minute	0.1	1	10	100
Typical number of counts, n	10	100	1000	10 000
Uncertainty in number of counts, $\sqrt{n}$	3	10	32	100
Fractional uncertainty in number of counts, $\sqrt{n}/n = 1/\sqrt{n}$	0.3	0.1	0.03	0.01
Uncertainty in number of counts per minute, $\sqrt{n}/t$, measured in minute^{-1}	30	10	3	1

Another way to appreciate the improvement that results from counting for a longer period is to compare the values of the uncertainty in the number of counts per minute, which are displayed in row 5 of Table 5.3. These were calculated by dividing the uncertainties in row 3 by the corresponding times in row 1: they show a similar improvement with increasing time (and number of counts) to that shown by the fractional uncertainties.

Unfortunately, the rate at which the fractional uncertainties fall with increasing n is frustratingly slow. For example, to reduce the fractional uncertainty by a factor of 10, the number of counts must be increased by a factor of 100. Of course, that requires counting for a period that is 100 times longer. So one of the skills every experimentalist needs to develop is the ability to decide how to balance the time invested in an experiment against the precision and accuracy of the result.

Question 5.3 Emission and absorption of photons are random processes, though this randomness is only apparent when the numbers of photons are small, that is when the intensity of the electromagnetic radiation is weak. In a particular experiment, 256 X-ray photons were counted in a period of 10.0 seconds.

(a) What is the uncertainty associated with this number, and what is the percentage uncertainty?

(b) If we required an uncertainty of less than 1% in the number of photons counted, for how long would we need to count? ■

5.4 Estimating systematic uncertainties

Systematic uncertainties and random uncertainties are often both present in the same measurement, and their effects were illustrated in Figures 4.4 and 4.5. The spread of repeated measurements allows us to estimate the size of the random uncertainties, and averaging the measurements tends to cancel out the effects of such uncertainties. Unfortunately, systematic uncertainties are usually much more difficult to estimate. Repeated readings do not show up the presence of systematic uncertainties, and no amount of averaging will reduce their effects.

Systematic uncertainties often arise from the measuring instrument used. For example, a metre rule may in fact be 1.005 m long, so that all measurements made with it are systematically 0.5% too short. Or a voltmeter may systematically read a higher voltage than the true value. Systematic uncertainties like these can often be discovered and estimated by calibrating the measuring instrument against a more accurate and reliable instrument. If this can be done, the measured results can be corrected and so the effects of this type of systematic uncertainty can be reduced, possibly to a level that is negligible compared with other uncertainties.

Another common type of systematic uncertainty is a 'zero uncertainty'. A screw gauge (Figure 4.3) may have deposits on its jaws, so that even when the jaws are closed the gauge reads 0.1 mm. This means that all lengths measured with the gauge will systematically appear 0.1 mm longer than they are. Or an ammeter may read –0.3 mA when it is not connected to a circuit, so that all measured currents are 0.3 mA low. However, once noted and recorded, this type of systematic uncertainty is straightforward to eliminate by subtracting the zero error from the measured values.

You may yourself introduce systematic uncertainties into an experiment. In timing 10 swings of a pendulum you might always tend to start the stopwatch late and stop it too early, so that the measured period is too short. Such uncertainties can best be detected by changing the way in which the experiment is done. For example, the timing uncertainty might show up if you compared the values for the period calculated from measurements of the times for 5, 10 and 20 swings of the pendulum.

Systematic uncertainties can also arise for other reasons that were noted in Section 4.2: observations affecting the measurement, extraneous influences affecting the measurement, and unrepresentative samples. In general, additional experiments are needed to check for the presence of such uncertainties and to estimate their magnitude.

It is important here to distinguish between systematic uncertainties that you can measure and allow for — and which, therefore, will *not* contribute to the uncertainty in the final result — and systematic uncertainties for which you can only say that they are 'likely to be $\pm x$'. For example, in the water-flow experiment discussed in Section 5.1, the two different kinds of systematic uncertainty could occur when timing the four-minute interval. Perhaps the stopwatch runs slow; comparing it with the telephone talking clock might show that it lost 10 s in one hour, which means that periods measured with the stopwatch need to be scaled up by a factor of 3600/3590 to get the actual period. If this calibration correction is made, then the slow running of the watch would not contribute to the uncertainties in the experiment. The calibration procedure eliminates this systematic uncertainty. However, you might have a tendency to start or stop the stopwatch too early or too late each time. You wouldn't *know* that such a systematic uncertainty was present, but it is certainly possible. A reasonable estimate for the possible size of such an uncertainty is ±0.2 s, since anything longer would probably be detected. This uncertainty of ±0.2 s in

240 s, or ±1 part in 1200, would lead to an uncertainty of ±1 part in 1200 in the volume of water collected. If the average volume of water collected was 436.6 cm^3, this would lead to an uncertainty of ±436.6 cm^3/1200 = ±0.4 cm^3.

So the difference between these two types of systematic uncertainty is that we know that one is definitely present, and we can measure and correct for its effect, whereas the other may or may not be present, and we can only make an educated guess at its possible magnitude. Essentially, once we have identified, measured and corrected for the first type of uncertainty, it ceases to be a source of uncertainty in the final result.

So your aim as an experimenter is to look critically at your experiment — at the instruments, the methods of measurement, the techniques that you use — and to identify and quantify the uncertainties that may be present. You may need to calibrate instruments, or make measurements with different instruments, or use alternative techniques, in order to do this. You can then decide whether you need to attempt to reduce the systematic uncertainties.

Question 5.4 The answer to Question 4.1 identifies possible random and systematic uncertainties in an experiment to measure the acceleration due to gravity. Suggest how each of the systematic uncertainties in the experiment could be reduced. ■

6 Combining uncertain quantities

In most experiments, more than one source of uncertainty will be present. Several random and systematic uncertainties may contribute to the uncertainty in measurements of a single quantity. In addition, measurements of a number of different quantities (each of which has an uncertainty associated with it) may have to be combined to calculate the required result. Therefore, it is important to know how these different uncertainties are combined to determine the overall uncertainty in the final result of an experiment.

It is not our aim here to get involved in statistical theories, so the rules for combining uncertainties will be presented without proof. The major objective is that you should be able to choose and apply the appropriate methods for combining uncertainties in the experimental work you are engaged in.

6.1 The uncertainty in a mean value

The standard deviation s of a set of measurements tells us about how widely scattered the measurements are — it indicates how far the individual measurements are likely to be from the mean value. Now we usually take the mean value of the measurements as our best estimate of the 'true' value, and so what we really need to know is how far the mean value is likely to be from the 'true' value. In other words, we want to know the uncertainty in the mean value.

We'll consider again the hypothetical experiment involving measurement of the force required to break a copper wire, which was introduced in Section 5.2, and we will assume that the normal distribution in Figure 6.1a represents the distribution of a very large number of measurements of this breaking force. Suppose that we make five measurements of the force, and calculate the mean value of these five measurements. We then repeat this process nine times, so that we end up with ten values of the mean, each of which is based on five different measurements. Figure 6.1b shows what these measurements and their mean values might look like.

● Is the spread of the 10 red marks that indicate the mean values in Figure 6.1b greater than, smaller than, or the same as, the spread of the individual measurements of force? Explain the reason for your answer.

❍ The spread of the means from the 10 sets of measurements, that is, the spread of the red marks in Figure 6.1b, is *smaller* than the spread of individual measurements, which is represented by the width of the distribution curve shown in Figure 6.1a. This is because a set of 5 measurements will almost certainly include some that are greater than the true mean $\langle F \rangle$ and some that are smaller. Therefore, when the mean of 5 measurements is calculated, it will be closer to the true mean $\langle F \rangle$ than most of the 5 individual measurements are.

● Suppose that you repeated the process described above, but with sets of 20 measurements, rather than sets of 5 measurements. Would you expect the spread of the means from the 10 sets of 20 measurements to be greater than, smaller than, or the same as, the spread of the means from the 10 sets of 5 measurements?

❍ The means from the sets of 20 measurements will have a *smaller* spread than the means from the sets of 5 measurements. The larger the number of measurements in a set, the smaller the statistical fluctuations in their mean value, and the closer the mean will lie to the mean of a very large number of measurements. ■

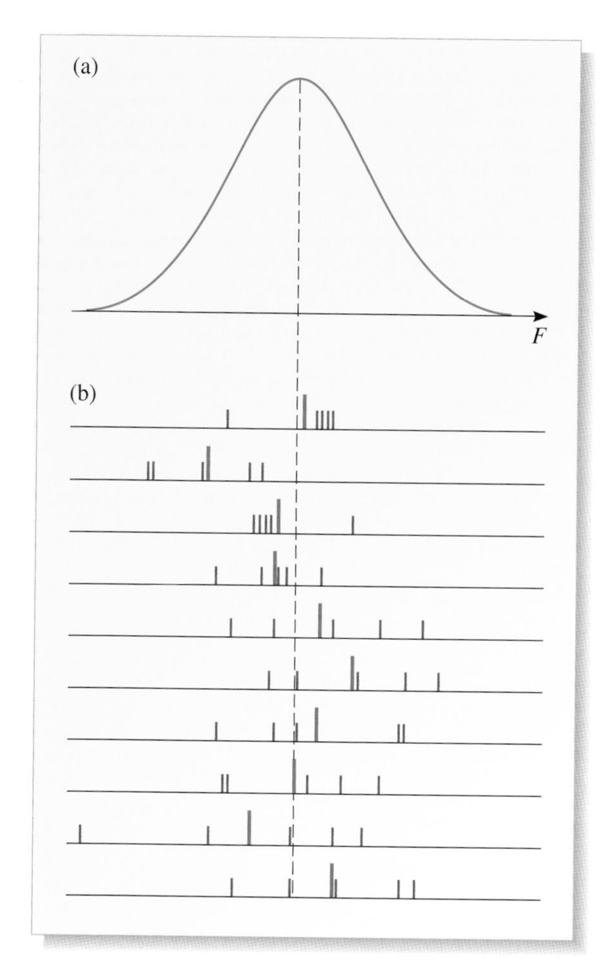

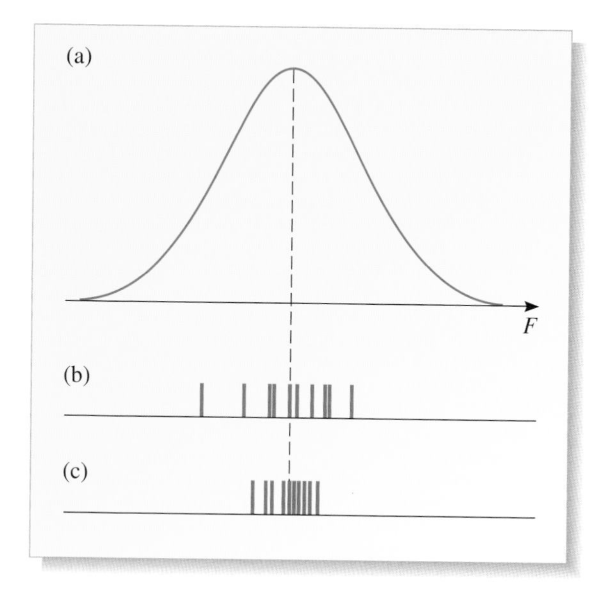

Figure 6.2 (a) The normal distribution curve for measurements of the force F required to break a wire. (b) 10 values of the mean breaking force, each calculated from a set of 5 measurements; these means are less spread out than the individual measurements. (c) Values of the means from 10 sets of 20 measurements each; these means are less spread out than the means of 5 measurements shown in (b).

Figure 6.1 (a) A normal distribution curve for measurements of the force F required to break copper wire of a certain diameter. The vertical axis is the frequency with which a particular value of F causes the wire to break. (b) The blue marks on each of the ten scales indicate five measurements of force, and each red mark indicates the mean value of the set of five measurements on that scale.

This is illustrated in Figure 6.2, which shows the distribution curve from Figure 6.1a, together with the 10 values of the means from the sets of 5 measurements in Figure 6.1b and 10 values of the means from sets of 20 measurements. The means from the 5-measurement sets are less widely scattered than the distribution of individual measurements, and the means from the 20-measurement sets are even less scattered.

This is an important result, with far-reaching implications for experimental work.

> The uncertainty in a mean value *decreases* as the number of measurements used to calculate the mean *increases*.

In other words, you can reduce the uncertainties in an experiment by increasing the number of measurements that you make.

Let's now make this statement about the uncertainty of a mean value quantitative.

The uncertainty s_m in a mean value that is derived from n measurements that have a standard deviation s is

$$s_m = \frac{s}{\sqrt{n-1}}. \quad (6.1)$$

We will refer to s_m as the **uncertainty in the mean**. It is usually referred to as the *standard error in the mean*, but as we explained in Section 4 we prefer to avoid the term error in this context.

We will not derive the important relationship in Equation 6.1 here; you should refer to an introductory statistics textbook if you are interested in the derivation.

It is important to note the effect of the square root that appears in Equation 6.1. If we take 5 measurements, then $\sqrt{n-1} = 2$, so s_m is $0.5s$. If we take 10 times as many measurements, i.e. 50 measurements, then $\sqrt{n-1} = 7$, so $s_m = 0.14s$. So for the increased effort of taking 10 times more measurements, we only reduce the uncertainty in the mean by $\sqrt{50-1}/\sqrt{5-1}$, which is approximately $\sqrt{10}$.

The significance of the uncertainty in the mean can be brought out in the following way. Suppose we make many sets of n measurements, and evaluate the mean for each set. Then the width of the distribution of the means will be characterized by the uncertainty in the mean s_m rather than by the standard deviation s. So whereas the standard deviation tells us about the scatter of individual measurements, the uncertainty in the mean of n measurements tells us about the scatter of the mean values that are each derived from n measurements.

If we assume that the mean values have a normal distribution, then we can be more explicit about the meaning of the uncertainty in the mean s_m. Suppose that the mean value is (10.4 ± 0.3) mm, where $s_m = 0.3$ mm is the uncertainty in the mean. This does *not* indicate that the true value necessarily lies within ± 0.3 mm of the mean value of 10.4 mm. If the mean values have a normal distribution, then there is a 68% probability that the mean value lies within $\pm s_m = \pm 0.3$ mm of the true value, a 95% probability that it lies within $\pm 2s_m = \pm 0.6$ mm of the true value, and a 99.7% probability that it lies within $\pm 3s_m = \pm 0.9$ mm of the true value. Conversely, we can say that there is a 68% probability that the true value lies within $\pm s_m$ of the mean value, a 95% probability that the true value lies within $\pm 2s_m$ of the mean value and a 99.7% probability that the true value lies within $\pm 3s_m$ of the mean value.

Question 6.1 Ten measurements are made of the diameter of a silver wire. The mean value of these measurements is 0.785 mm and their standard deviation is 0.006 mm.

(a) What uncertainty should be quoted for the mean diameter?

(b) Are the measurements consistent with a 'true' value for the diameter of 0.791 mm?

(c) If the mean value needed to be known with a precision of ± 0.001 mm, how many measurements of the diameter would have to be made? ■

6.2 Combining uncertainties in a single quantity

Let's return to the example of a water-flow experiment discussed in Section 4.3, and consider how we would combine a systematic uncertainty of $\pm 0.5\ \text{cm}^3$ arising from the calibration of the measuring container and a random uncertainty of $\pm 0.4\ \text{cm}^3$ in the volume of water collected. The obvious answer might seem to be to add them directly to get a total uncertainty of $0.5\,\text{cm}^3 + 0.4\,\text{cm}^3 = 0.9\,\text{cm}^3$. But this really gives an unduly pessimistic assessment of the uncertainty. After all, the random uncertainty and the systematic uncertainty are entirely *independent*, so it is highly unlikely (though possible, of course) that, for any given measurement, these two uncertainties will both be at their maximum positive values, or at their maximum negative values. There will generally be a partial cancellation of the two uncertainties. So the rule that we use for combining two *independent* uncertainties in the *same* quantity X is

$$\delta X = \sqrt{\delta x_1^2 + \delta x_2^2}, \tag{6.2}$$

where δX is the overall uncertainty, and δx_1 and δx_2 are the individual uncertainties that are to be combined. Thus, in the water-flow example,

$$\begin{aligned}\delta X &= \sqrt{(0.5\,\text{cm}^3)^2 + (0.4\,\text{cm}^3)^2}\\ &= \sqrt{0.25\,\text{cm}^6 + 0.16\,\text{cm}^6}\\ &= \sqrt{0.41\,\text{cm}^6}\\ &= 0.6\,\text{cm}^3.\end{aligned}$$

This uncertainty is larger than either of the contributing uncertainties, but considerably smaller than their sum.

If more than two uncertainties are involved, then the method follows the same principle. Suppose that we think that there is an additional systematic uncertainty of $\pm 0.3\,\text{cm}^3$ in measuring the volume of water collected. Then the overall uncertainty is

$$\begin{aligned}\delta X &= \sqrt{(0.5\,\text{cm}^3)^2 + (0.4\,\text{cm}^3)^2 + (0.3\,\text{cm}^3)^2}\\ &= 0.7\,\text{cm}^3\end{aligned}$$

Again, this is larger than the individual uncertainties, but smaller than their sum.

To summarize:

Independent uncertainties δx_1, δx_2, δx_3, ... in a measured quantity X will give rise to an overall uncertainty δX given by

$$\delta X = \sqrt{\delta x_1^2 + \delta x_2^2 + \delta x_3^2 + \ldots}. \tag{6.3}$$

When uncertainties are not independent, they are much more difficult to deal with, unless the form of the dependence is known precisely. Their dependence might mean, for example, that a large positive uncertainty from one source was always associated with a large negative uncertainty from another source, thus leading to cancellation, and an overall uncertainty that was much smaller than the individual uncertainties. Alternatively, a positive uncertainty from one source may always be associated with a positive uncertainty from another source, so that the overall uncertainty is really more like the sum of the individual uncertainties. No simple rules can be given for dealing with dependent uncertainties, and each case must be analysed individually.

Question 6.2 The manufacturer of a precision digital voltmeter specifies that the uncertainty of the instrument's reading is a combination of ±0.015% of the reading, ±0.0015% of the full-scale reading of the scale used and ±1 in the final digit displayed. If the instrument displays a voltage of 30.511 mV on the 200 mV range, what uncertainty should be quoted with this value? ■

6.3 Combining uncertainties in sums, differences, products, ratios and powers

In Section 6.2, we were concerned with combining uncertainties in a *single* measured quantity to find the total uncertainty in that quantity. However, the aim of many experiments is to evaluate something that depends on *several* measured quantities, *each* of which has its own uncertainty.

As an example, suppose that you are determining the density ρ of a block of metal by measuring its mass m and its volume V, and then using the relationship $\rho = m/V$. How is the uncertainty in ρ related to the uncertainties in m and V?

Table 6.1 gives a set of rules, from which you can select the appropriate one to apply in a given situation. For example, for the ratio of two quantities, m/V, you would use Equation 6.5.

Table 6.1 Rules for combining uncertainties. The first column lists various relationships between a quantity X and measured quantities A, B, C, D, which have uncertainties δA, δB, δC, δD. The second column indicates how the uncertainty δX in X is related to the uncertainties δA, δB, δC, δD.

Dependence of X on A, B, C, D	Expression used to calculate δX	
$X = A \pm B$	$\delta X = \sqrt{\delta A^2 + \delta B^2}$	(6.4)
$X = AB$ or $X = A/B$	$\dfrac{\delta X}{X} = \sqrt{\left(\dfrac{\delta A}{A}\right)^2 + \left(\dfrac{\delta B}{B}\right)^2}$	(6.5)
$X = A^n$	$\dfrac{\delta X}{X} = n\,\dfrac{\delta A}{A}$	(6.6)
When a constant k is involved:		
$X = kA$	$\delta X = k\,\delta A$, or equivalently $\dfrac{\delta X}{X} = \dfrac{\delta A}{A}$	(6.7) (6.8)
$X = kA + B$	$\delta X = \sqrt{(k\,\delta A)^2 + (\delta B)^2}$	(6.9)
$X = kAB$ or $X = kA/B$	$\dfrac{\delta X}{X} = \sqrt{\left(\dfrac{\delta A}{A}\right)^2 + \left(\dfrac{\delta B}{B}\right)^2}$	(6.10)
$X = kA^n$	$\dfrac{\delta X}{X} = n\,\dfrac{\delta A}{A}$	(6.11)
When more than two quantities are involved:		
$X = A + B - C + D + \ldots$	$\delta X = \sqrt{\delta A^2 + \delta B^2 + \delta C^2 + \delta D^2 + \ldots}$	(6.12)
$X = (A \times B)/(C \times D)$	$\dfrac{\delta X}{X} = \sqrt{\left(\dfrac{\delta A}{A}\right)^2 + \left(\dfrac{\delta B}{B}\right)^2 + \left(\dfrac{\delta C}{C}\right)^2 + \left(\dfrac{\delta D}{D}\right)^2}$	(6.13)
When a function of a variable is involved:		
$X = f(A)$	$\delta X = f(A + \delta A) - f(A)$, or equivalently $\delta X \approx \dfrac{\mathrm{d}f(A)}{\mathrm{d}A}\,\delta A$ (see text below)	(6.14) (6.15)

There are several important points to note about the expressions for the uncertainties in Table 6.1.

- Only + signs appear under the square roots in the expressions for δX and $\delta X/X$, irrespective of whether the function is a sum or difference, or product or ratio.
- The constant k has *no* effect on the *fractional* uncertainty $\delta X/X$. This is the reason that Equations 6.10 and 6.11 are identical to Equations 6.5 and 6.6, respectively.
- Percentage uncertainties can be used in place of fractional uncertainties in the equations in Table 6.1. The percentage uncertainty in X is related to the fractional uncertainty $\delta X/X$ in the following way:

$$\text{percentage uncertainty in } X = \frac{\delta X}{X} \times 100.$$

Take Equation 6.5, for example. In this case,

$$\begin{aligned}
\%\text{ uncertainty in } X &= \frac{\delta X}{X} \times 100 \\
&= 100\sqrt{\left(\frac{\delta A}{A}\right)^2 + \left(\frac{\delta B}{B}\right)^2} \\
&= \sqrt{10^4 \times \left[\left(\frac{\delta A}{A}\right)^2 + \left(\frac{\delta B}{B}\right)^2\right]} \\
&= \sqrt{\left(100\frac{\delta A}{A}\right)^2 + \left(100\frac{\delta B}{B}\right)^2} \\
&= \sqrt{(\%\text{ uncertainty in } A)^2 + (\%\text{ uncertainty in } B)^2}.
\end{aligned}$$

Uncertainties in functions

As well as combining uncertainties in quantities that appear as sums, differences, products, ratios or powers, you will also need to evaluate uncertainties in cases that involve a function of the measured quantity. For example, if $X = e^A$, and the uncertainty in A is $\pm\delta A$, then what is the uncertainty $\pm\delta X$ in X?

The relationship between δX and δA is illustrated in Figure 6.3a. When the value of A changes from A_0 to $A_0 + \delta A$ then the value of X changes from X_0 to $X_0 + \delta X$. So the simplest way to find δX is to work out the values of X corresponding to A_0 and $A_0 + \delta A$:

$$X_0 = e^{A_0}$$

$$X_0 + \delta X = e^{(A_0 + \delta A)}.$$

Subtracting the first equation from the second:

$$\delta X = e^{(A_0 + \delta A)} - e^{A_0}. \tag{6.16}$$

Note that the value of δX depends on the value of A_0 as well as depending on the value of δA. This is because the exponential function is non-linear: in regions where the curve is steeper, there will be a greater change δX for a given change δA.

So to evaluate the uncertainty δX in the function $X = e^A$ when $A = 1$ and $\delta A = 0.1$, we use Equation 6.16:

$$\delta X = e^{1.1} - e^1 = 3.004 - 2.718 = 0.286 = 0.3 \text{ to one significant figure.}$$

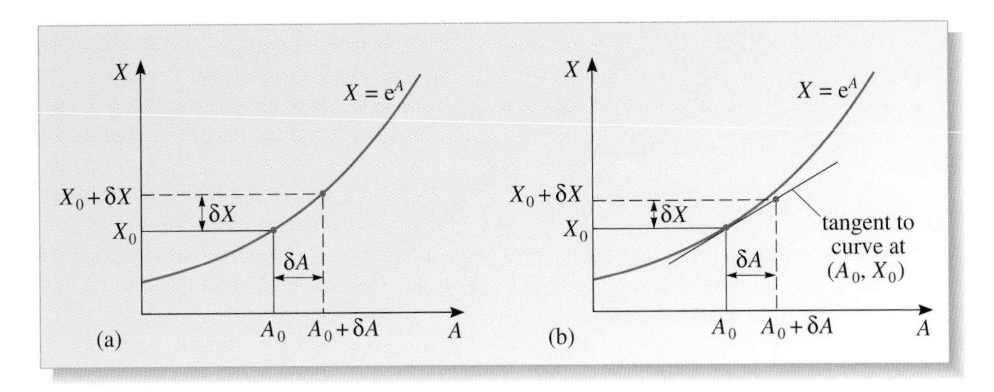

Figure 6.3 (a) A graph of $X = e^A$. When A increases from A_0 to $A_0 + \delta A$, the value of X increases from X_0 to $X_0 + \delta X$. (b) The same graph as in (a), with a tangent drawn at $A = A_0$. Here the value of δX is estimated using the gradient of the tangent, and is smaller than the value deduced in part (a) using the curve.

Compare this with the uncertainty in X when $A = 2$, and $\delta A = 0.1$, i.e. the same value as before:

$$\delta X = e^{2.1} - e^2 = 8.166 - 7.389 = 0.777 = 0.8 \text{ to one significant figure.}$$

The large difference between the two values of δX underlines the need to calculate the uncertainty δX for *each* different value of A, even if the uncertainties δA are all the same.

More generally, if $X = f(A)$, then the uncertainty δX is related to the uncertainty δA by

$$\delta X = f(A + \delta A) - f(A). \tag{6.14}$$

An alternative method of calculating values for δX is to use the standard result from calculus

$$\delta X \approx \frac{\mathrm{d}f(A)}{\mathrm{d}A}\,\delta A\,. \tag{6.15}$$

Using this result is equivalent to approximating the curve by its tangent, as shown in Figure 6.3b, and this is a reasonable approximation when the uncertainties are small (i.e. less than about 10%). For the exponential function that we used in the example above,

$$\delta X \approx \frac{\mathrm{d}(e^A)}{\mathrm{d}A}\delta A = e^A\,\delta A.$$

So when $A = 1$ and $\delta A = 0.1$, this expression gives $\delta X \approx e^1 \times 0.1 = 0.272$. Note that this is slightly different from the value that we calculated above, but to one significant figure the results are the same.

Bear in mind that you are not expected to understand the statistical theory that leads to the various equations for combining uncertainties. You should regard them as recipes, and refer to them and apply them as necessary. The following examples illustrate their use.

Example 6.1

The temperature of a liquid in an insulated container was initially measured as (16.2 ± 0.4) °C, and after heating the liquid for a short period the temperature had increased to (22.7 ± 0.4) °C. What was the temperature rise θ?

Solution

The temperature rise θ is given by

$$\begin{aligned}\theta &= (\theta_2 - \theta_1)\\ &= (22.7 - 16.2)\,°\text{C}\\ &= 6.5\,°\text{C}.\end{aligned}$$

Since we need to find the uncertainty in the *difference* between two quantities, we use Equation 6.4:

$$\begin{aligned}\delta\theta &= \sqrt{(\delta\theta_1)^2 + (\delta\theta_2)^2}\\ &= \sqrt{(0.4\,°\text{C})^2 + (0.4\,°\text{C})^2}\\ &= 0.6\,°\text{C}.\end{aligned}$$

So we can quote the temperature difference as $\theta = (6.5 \pm 0.6)$ °C.

Example 6.2

The velocity v_x of a train is measured as $(80 \pm 5)\,\text{km h}^{-1}$ over a measured time t of (0.20 ± 0.02) hours. What distance x does the train travel in this time?

Solution

The distance travelled x is

$$\begin{aligned}x &= v_x t\\ &= (80\,\text{km h}^{-1}) \times (0.20\,\text{h})\\ &= 16\,\text{km}.\end{aligned}$$

In this case, we are using a product of two quantities to calculate the distance, so the uncertainty δx must be calculated from Equation 6.5 in Table 6.1:

$$\frac{\delta x}{x} = \sqrt{\left(\frac{\delta v_x}{v_x}\right)^2 + \left(\frac{\delta t}{t}\right)^2}$$

$$\begin{aligned}\frac{\delta x}{16\,\text{km}} &= \sqrt{\left(\frac{5\,\text{km h}^{-1}}{80\,\text{km h}^{-1}}\right)^2 + \left(\frac{0.02\,\text{h}}{0.20\,\text{h}}\right)^2}\\ &= \sqrt{3.9 \times 10^{-3} + 10^{-2}}\\ &= 0.12.\end{aligned}$$

Therefore

$$\delta x = 0.12 \times 16\,\text{km} \approx 2\,\text{km}.$$

The result is, therefore, $x = (16 \pm 2)$ km.

Example 6.3

The diameter of a sphere is measured to be (7.2 ± 0.5) cm. What is its volume?

Solution

Volume of a sphere $V = 4\pi r^3/3$, where r is the radius, so in terms of the diameter $d = 2r$, we have

$$V = \frac{\pi d^3}{6}$$
$$= 1.95 \times 10^2\ \text{cm}^3.$$

Using Equation 6.11 in Table 6.1,

$$\frac{\delta V}{V} = \frac{3\delta d}{d} = \frac{3 \times 0.5\ \text{cm}}{7.2\ \text{cm}} = 0.21.$$

$$\delta V = 0.21 \times (1.95 \times 10^2\ \text{cm}^3) = 41\ \text{cm}^3.$$

So the volume is $V = (2.0 \pm 0.4) \times 10^2\ \text{cm}^3$.

Note that the fractional uncertainty in the volume is *three times* larger than the fractional uncertainty in the measured diameter. Because uncertainties increase so rapidly when powers are taken, you should always take particular care to reduce uncertainties when measuring quantities that will be raised to some power. Note also that it would be *wrong* to reason that since

$$V = \frac{\pi}{3} \times d \times d \times d,$$

then
$$\frac{\delta V}{V} = \sqrt{\left(\frac{\delta d}{d}\right)^2 + \left(\frac{\delta d}{d}\right)^2 + \left(\frac{\delta d}{d}\right)^2}$$
$$= \sqrt{3}\frac{\delta d}{d}. \qquad \text{[WRONG]}$$

This is wrong because the equation for the uncertainty in a product assumes that the uncertainties that are being combined are independent, so it *cannot* be used in this case. Here the three terms that have to be multiplied are exactly the same and therefore certainly not independent.

Question 6.3 A current of (8.5 ± 0.2) A flows through a heating element when a voltage of (12.2 ± 0.4) V is applied across its terminals. What is the power dissipated? [*Reminder*: Power P (in watts) = current (in amps) × voltage difference (in volts).]

Question 6.4 Three resistors have resistances of $(82 \pm 5)\ \Omega$, $330\ \Omega \pm 5\%$ and $1200\ \Omega \pm 1\%$. What is the total resistance of the three resistors when they are connected in series?

Question 6.5 The velocity v_z of a falling object increases from $(1.7 \pm 0.5)\ \text{m s}^{-1}$ to $(58 \pm 1)\ \text{m s}^{-1}$ in an interval of (5.5 ± 0.2) s. What is the mean acceleration of the object?

Question 6.6 When light is diffracted by a diffraction grating with line spacing d, the first order of diffraction for a spectral line of wavelength λ occurs at an angle θ given by

$$\lambda = d \sin \theta. \tag{6.17}$$

What is the wavelength of a red line whose first order of diffraction occurs at $24.1° \pm 0.1°$, if the line spacing $d = (1.655 \pm 0.005) \times 10^{-6}$ m? ■

6.4 Some common sense about uncertainties

The examples and questions in the previous subsection illustrate a few general points that are worth highlighting. First, uncertainties, by their very nature, cannot be precisely quantified. So a statement like $l = (2.732 \pm 0.312)$ m is rather silly, and this result should be quoted as $l = (2.7 \pm 0.3)$ m. As a general rule:

> Uncertainties should usually be quoted to one significant figure; two significant figures are sometimes justified, particularly if the first figure is a 1.

You should bear this in mind when trying to assess the magnitudes of uncertainties and when doing calculations involving uncertainties.

Secondly, you can safely neglect small uncertainties. The total uncertainty in a result may be a combination of several contributing uncertainties, and these contributing uncertainties may have widely varying sizes. But, because the uncertainties (or fractional uncertainties) are combined as the sum of the squares, as a general rule:

> When calculating uncertainties in *sums and differences*, ignore any uncertainties that are less than one-third of the largest uncertainty.
>
> When calculating uncertainties in *products and ratios*, ignore any *fractional* uncertainties that are less than one-third of the largest *fractional* uncertainty.

Thirdly, concentrate your experimental efforts on reducing the dominant uncertainties. As we have just shown, the largest uncertainties will dominate the uncertainty in the final result, and small uncertainties can often be neglected. Therefore, it is very important when doing experiments not to waste a lot of time reducing small uncertainties when much larger uncertainties are present.

> Find out as early as possible in an experiment what the dominant uncertainties are, and then concentrate your time and effort on reducing them.

Finally, take particular care when differences and powers are involved. Suppose that you measure two angles in an experiment, $\theta_1 = (73 \pm 3)$ degrees and $\theta_2 = (65 \pm 3)$ degrees, and you then calculate the difference, i.e. $\theta = \theta_1 - \theta_2 = 8$ degrees. The uncertainty is

$$\begin{aligned} \Delta\theta &= \sqrt{(\delta\theta_1)^2 + (\delta\theta_2)^2} \\ &= \sqrt{3^2 + 3^2} \text{ degrees} = 4 \text{ degrees.} \end{aligned}$$

So $\theta = (8 \pm 4)$ degrees. This is a 50% uncertainty compared with only about 4% in the individual measurements!

To take another example, suppose you measure an edge of a cube as $l = (6.0 \pm 0.5)$ mm, and then calculate the volume: $V = l^3 = 216\,\text{mm}^3$. The uncertainty is given by

$$\frac{\delta V}{V} = \frac{3\delta l}{l} = \frac{3 \times 0.5}{6}.$$

Because the volume is the third power of the length, the fractional uncertainty in the volume is three times greater than the fractional uncertainty in the length measurement. As a general rule:

> If the calculation of an experimental result involves taking the difference of two nearly equal measured quantities, or taking the power of a measured quantity, then pay particular attention to reducing the uncertainties in those quantities.

7 Analysing experimental data

After making various measurements, and estimating their uncertainties, the data then has to be processed in some way to obtain the final result. You may think that this part of an experiment is rather trivial compared with setting up the equipment and making the measurements, but carelessness at this stage can ruin an experiment. So here are a few hints that should help you to analyse your data with a minimum of effort and a maximum chance of ending up with an appropriate answer.

(a) Have you recorded all data necessary for the analysis? This first point is a reiteration of what was said in Section 3.1 about keeping records in your laboratory notebook. It is vital that you record all of the necessary data and information that you will need to calculate the final result. If you leave the laboratory, or dismantle the apparatus, and then discover that you omitted to record a vital piece of data needed to analyse your results, your whole experiment may be worthless. Among the things that you might forget to record are the range of a meter, the ambient temperature or the calibration factor for an instrument. In this context, it is worth saying that a clearly laid out notebook will make it much easier for you to check what you have, and what you haven't, recorded.

(b) Plan your data analysis Before you start to do any calculations with your data, think carefully about how you will calculate the final result. You may need to combine algebraic equations, and rearrange them so that the quantity that you want to calculate is the subject of the equation. After doing this, it is advisable to check that the expression that you've derived is correct. One way to do this is by checking the consistency of the units on either side of the equation. Alternatively, you can ask yourself whether the dependence of the subject of the equation on the other variables is what you would expect.

It's a good idea to think about how you will analyse the data when you are planning the measurements that you will make. This will allow you to leave appropriate space in your laboratory notebook for extra columns in data tables, if they are needed for the analysis stage. It is also worthwhile developing the habit of laying out calculations neatly, and spacing them out. You are much less likely to make errors if your results are easy to read.

(c) Substitute numerical values at the end of the analysis It is good practice to leave the substitution of numerical data into equations until the latest possible stage of a calculation. Here are a couple of examples:

- Calibration of a ruler against a standard shows that all lengths measured with this ruler need to be corrected by multiplying by a factor of 1.006. If you measured ten values of a particular length, you could multiply each by 1.006 and then work out the mean value. However, it would be much more economical of your time to calculate the mean of the ten uncorrected values and then apply the correction factor once to the mean value.
- In an experiment to determine Young's modulus Y for a wire, you measure the extension e of the wire when various masses m are suspended from it. The modulus is defined as $Y = mgl/Ae$, where l is the length of the wire and A is its cross-sectional area. You could use each pair of values of e and m to calculate a value of Y, but it would be more efficient to calculate the ratio m/e for each pair of values, then average the values of the ratio, and then finally multiply (once) by gl/A to calculate Y. (It would be even better to plot a graph of e versus m, and calculate the value of m/e from the gradient, and we will discuss this approach in Section 8.3.)

Of course, in each of these examples, reducing the number of calculations not only saves you time, but also reduces the chances of making an error in a calculation.

(d) Check your calculations The use of calculators and computers has reduced the time and tedium required to analyse data, and allows many methods of data analysis to be used routinely now, where previously they were very time-consuming. However, it is important to check the results of calculations, as it is incredibly easy to key an incorrect number into a calculator or to make a simple slip in mental arithmetic. One way to check a calculation is to repeat it in a different order. For example, if you calculated the value of the expression

$$\frac{6.63 \times 10^{-34} \times 2.998 \times 10^{8}}{542 \times 10^{-9} \times 1.602 \times 10^{-19}} = 2.29$$

in the order

$$6.63 \times 10^{-34} \times 2.998 \times 10^{8} \,/\, 542 \times 10^{-9} \,/\, 1.602 \times 10^{-19},$$

then try it again in the order

$$2.998 \times 10^{8} \,/\, 1.602 \times 10^{-19} \times 6.63 \times 10^{-34} \,/\, 542 \times 10^{-9}.$$

Another check that you can do is to round the numbers in the expression and calculate the value of this approximate expression; it shouldn't differ from your previous calculation by more than a factor of about 3. So with the example above:

$$\frac{7 \times 10^{-34} \times 3 \times 10^{8}}{500 \times 10^{-9} \times 2 \times 10^{-19}} = \left(\frac{21}{1000}\right) \times 10^{(-34+8+9+19)} = 2.1.$$

It is always worth asking yourself whether the result that you have calculated seems reasonable. Of course, there will be occasions when you don't know what a reasonable value would be. Few physicists would remember the value of Young's modulus for copper. However, if a calculation of the speed of sound in air gave a value of $3.3\ \mathrm{m\,s^{-1}}$, alarm bells should ring and you should check the calculation.

In some situations there is a self-check built into a calculation so there is no need to repeat it. For example, if you are using a series of measurements to calculate values for a particular quantity, then an error in one of the calculations will produce an anomalous value, which you would then automatically check. Similarly, if you use your data to calculate a series of values that you plot on a graph, then calculation errors are likely to show up as deviations of a plotted point from the general trend shown by other measurements.

(e) Retain an appropriate number of digits in sequential calculations When you are performing a series of calculations, then it is important to record and carry forward an appropriate number of digits at each stage. The number of significant figures in your *measured* data should be such that the uncertainty that you quote affects the last digit (or possibly the last two digits, if you are quoting the uncertainty to two significant figures because it starts with a '1'). A calculator will generally work to more digits than you require, so in sequential calculations you will not lose any precision. However, if you round an intermediate result and record it in your notebook, and then use this rounded value in subsequent calculations, then you may lose some of the hard-won precision of the original data. It is therefore advisable to carry forward to later stages of a calculation *two more* digits than you are justified in quoting in your intermediate results. At the end of the data analysis, when you have worked out the overall uncertainty, you can round the final result to the appropriate number of significant figures.

For example, suppose that a constant force of $F_x = 2.03\,\text{N}$ causes an object to accelerate from rest to $3.2\,\text{m s}^{-1}$ in 9.3 s, and you want to know the acceleration a_x and the mass m of the object. You would first calculate the acceleration:

$$a_x = \frac{\Delta v_x}{\Delta t} = \frac{(3.2\,\text{m s}^{-1})}{9.3\,\text{s}} = 0.344\,086\,\text{m s}^{-2}.$$

and would quote this as $0.34\,\text{m s}^{-2}$, since the initial data was only known to two significant figures. Using this value to calculate the mass would give:

$$m = \frac{F_x}{a_x} = \frac{2.03\ \text{N}}{0.34\ \text{m s}^{-2}} = 5.970\,5882\,\text{kg}$$

which is 6.0 kg to two significant figures. However, it is better to retain two extra digits in the acceleration value (i.e. $0.3441\,\text{m s}^{-2}$) to use in the final step of the calculation, and this would give

$$m = \frac{F_x}{a_x} = \frac{2.03\ \text{N}}{0.3441\ \text{m s}^{-2}} = 5.899\,4478\,\text{kg}.$$

This is 5.9 kg to two significant figures, and this result is more accurate than the value of 6.0 kg that was obtained using only the two significant figures for the acceleration in the final calculation.

(f) Make appropriate use of graphs The results of experiments can often be analysed most effectively using graphical methods, and we will discuss these in the next section.

8 Making use of graphs

Table 8.1 Experimental measurements of the extension of a copper wire in response to different masses suspended from one end.

Mass/kg	Extension/mm
5.0	0.2
10.0	0.5
15.0	0.8
20.0	1.0
22.5	1.5
25.0	1.3
27.5	1.4
30.0	1.5
32.5	1.7
35.0	1.8
37.5	1.9
40.0	2.0
42.5	2.3
45.0	2.5
47.5	2.8
50.0	3.2

Physicists frequently use graphs to represent the results of their experiments, and some of the reasons for using graphs are well illustrated by comparing Table 8.1 with Figure 8.1. The table and the graph both summarize the results of the same experiment — an experiment in which the extension of a copper wire was measured when various masses were suspended from its end.

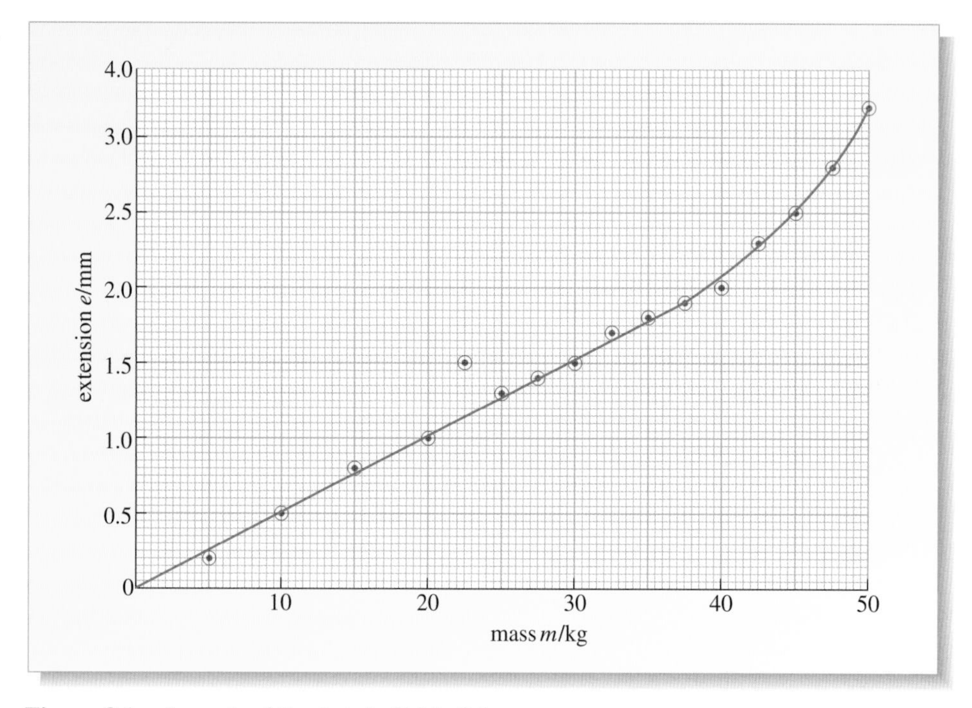

Figure 8.1 A graph of the data in Table 8.1.

After glancing at the graph, it is possible to deduce the following information.

- For masses up to about 35 kg, the extension is proportional to the mass, i.e. doubling the mass produces twice the extension.
- For masses greater than about 35 kg, the wire stretches more for a given increase in mass than it did below 35 kg, and indeed the extension is no longer proportional to mass above 35 kg.
- The points lie fairly close to the straight line (with one exception), and the uncertainties in the experimental measurements must be about ±0.05 mm in the extension, and/or ±1 kg in the mass.
- The point plotted at mass = 22.5 kg and extension = 1.5 mm is anomalous. It is much further from the line than any other point — in fact higher than the points for the next two larger masses — and ought to be checked.
- Very few of the points lie exactly on the straight line. For example, the extension that you would expect for a mass of 5 kg is larger than the measured value of 0.2 mm, and probably nearer 0.26 mm. The straight line drawn *averages* out experimental uncertainties in individual measurements.
- The extension that you would expect for a mass of 17 kg is 0.86 mm. In this case, the straight line on the graph is used to *interpolate* between measured values.
- The gradient of the straight line relating extension e to mass m (for $m < 35$ kg) is 1.52 mm/30 kg = 0.051 mm kg^{-1} and the intercept is zero. The equation describing the relationship between e and m is

$e = 0.051\ \mathrm{mm\,kg^{-1}} \times m.$

(We will discuss gradients, intercepts and equations of graphs in more detail in Section 8.3.)

All seven of the statements above could be made by analysing the data in Table 8.1 — after all, the graph was plotted using the information in the table. However, it would take much longer to deduce these statements from the tabulated information than from the graph. This demonstrates the great advantage of graphs as visual aids. The form of the relationship between measured quantities, the typical uncertainties in measurements and the presence of anomalous measurements are readily apparent. In addition, graphs allow straightforward averaging of experimental measurements, interpolation between measurements and (in simple cases) determination of the equation relating measured quantities.

Hopefully, you are convinced of the benefits of using graphs to display and analyse the results of your experiments! In Sections 8.2 to 8.4 we will discuss in more detail how to use graphs, but first check your awareness of good practice for graph plotting by answering the following question.

Question 8.1 Figure 8.2 shows a graph plotted by a student to display her results from a photoelectric-effect experiment. The data used to plot the graph are shown in Table 8.2. Use your prior knowledge and experience of graphs to make a list of up to ten criticisms of this graph. (You may assume that the individual data points have been plotted correctly.) ■

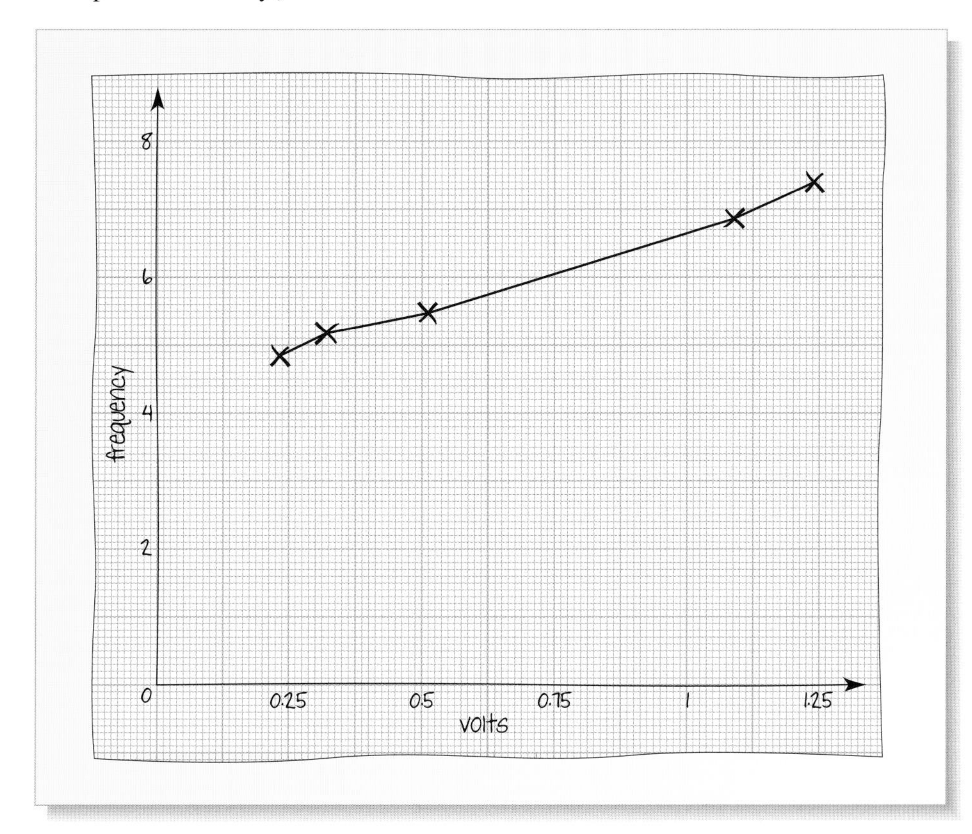

Figure 8.2 A graph plotted by a student to show the dependence of stopping voltage on frequency. In the experiment, the student measured the voltage that she needed to apply to a photocell in order to reduce the photoelectric current to zero. This was done for five different frequencies of light, i.e. five different spectral lines.

Table 8.2 The data from a photoelectric experiment that was used to plot the graph in Figure 8.2.

Frequency $/10^{14}$ Hz	Stopping voltage /V
7.40	1.24
6.88	1.09
5.49	0.51
5.19	0.32
4.85	0.23
uncertainty ±0.005	uncertainty ±0.04

8.1 Graph plotting: a checklist of good practice

There are a number of useful guidelines to good practice that are worth keeping in mind when you are plotting graphs of experimental data. We will summarize them briefly below.

(a) Plot the independent variable (the one you have control of) along the horizontal axis and the dependent variable along the vertical axis Plotting graphs in this way is purely a matter of convention, but it is a convention that is almost always followed in physics. In the experiment for which results are plotted in Figure 8.1, the experimenter decided what masses to suspend from the wire, so mass was the independent variable and was plotted on the horizontal axis. She measured how the extension *depended* on the mass, so extension was the *dependent* variable and was therefore plotted on the vertical axis.

(b) Label each axis with the name (or symbol) of the plotted quantity divided by its units We are then plotting pure numbers on the graph (see Box 3.1). In Figure 8.1, the extension of 1.3 mm was divided by the unit mm to get the pure number 1.3 that is plotted. This is made explicit by labelling the vertical axis 'extension e/mm'. In some cases it is helpful to also include powers of ten in the axis label to avoid a lot of zeroes or powers of ten with each of the numbers on the scale. So if you had to plot values of distance that were typically 2×10^{10} m, you could label the axis 'distance/10^{10} m' and then label the appropriate point on the scale as '2'. This would be preferable to labelling the axis 'distance/m' and labelling the scale point '2×10^{10}'.

(c) Choose the ranges of the scales so as to make good use of the graph paper You should try to avoid cramming all the points into one corner, or even one-half, of the graph (Figure 8.3). In some situations, it may not be necessary for the scale to go to zero on one or both of the axes. However, bear in mind that it is easy to misinterpret a graph if you don't notice the suppression of the zero of an axis — as politicians and advertisers know only too well!

(d) Choose a scale that makes plotting simple Scales in which ten small divisions of the graph paper are equal to 1, 10, 100, or any other power of ten are easiest to use. However, scales in which ten small divisions equal 2 or 5, or one of these numbers multiplied by a power of ten, are also manageable. Don't make your life difficult by choosing a scale in which ten small divisions represents 3 or 7; you would take much longer to plot the data, and the chance of plotting points incorrectly would be very much higher!

(e) Plot points clearly Tiny dots may be confused with dirt on the graph paper (or vice versa) and large dots make it difficult to read off the plotted values from the graph. Either small crosses × or dots with small circles around them ⊙ are recommended. If you are plotting a number of different sets of experimental data on a single graph — for example, pressure versus volume for three different temperatures — then it may be clearer if you use a different symbol for the data points for each of the three temperatures. You may find that it is worth plotting points using a pencil initially, so that they can easily be erased if plotted incorrectly.

(f) Plan your measurements to get a sensible spread of data points on the graph On a straight-line graph this usually means having the data points evenly spaced. However, if you need to determine an intercept, you may want additional points close to the axis. On a non-linear graph, it is usually advisable to concentrate your measurements in regions where the dependent variable changes rapidly.

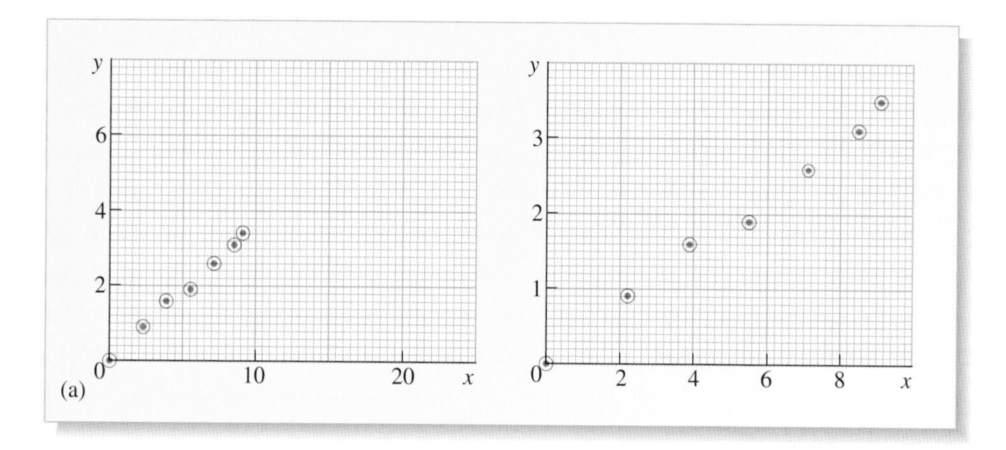

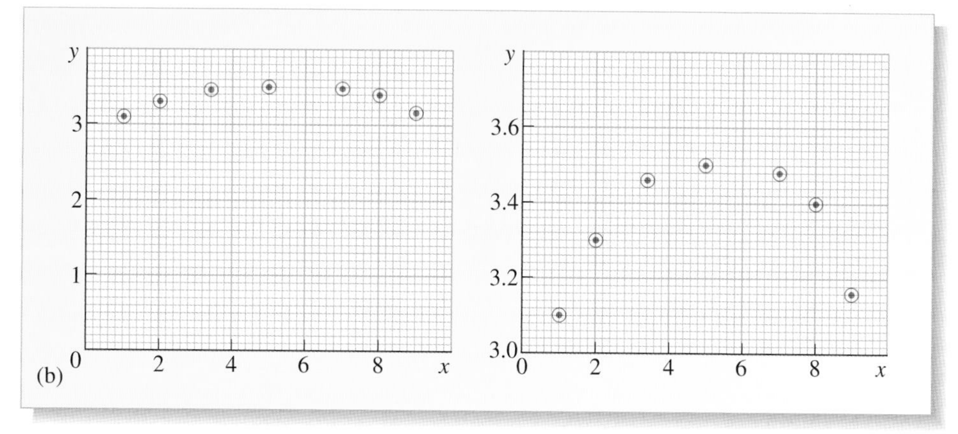

Figure 8.3 (a) These two graphs represent the same data, but the expanded scales in the graph on the right makes better use of the graph paper. (b) Another pair of graphs representing a different set of data from (a). The expanded scale on the vertical axis on the right-hand graph, which starts at 3.0 rather than 0, makes better use of the graph paper.

For example, if your graph shows a pronounced peak, you will need to make more measurements in the region where the dependent variable is increasing or decreasing rapidly — the steep slopes on the sides of the peak.

(g) Plot a graph of your results while you are collecting the data By plotting your data as you collect it, you will immediately notice whether your data points are sensibly spread out. You will also notice if any points are inconsistent with the general trend, and this might be a cue to repeat some of the measurements. It is sensible initially to use a pencil to label the axes and scales and to plot points, since there will be occasions when you decide that a different scale is more appropriate.

Plotting as you go will not always be possible. If you are measuring an effect that changes rapidly with time — a short-lived radioactive decay process, for example — then there may not be time between the measurements to plot the data. However, even in situations like this, it may be possible to plot-as-you-go if two or more people are collaborating on the experiment.

(h) Draw a straight line or a smooth curve to represent the general trend of the points on the graph It is seldom appropriate to represent the results of a physics experiment by a zigzag line connecting the data points. However, rather than drawing a curve to represent a trend, you may wish to draw a theoretical curve on the graph so that you can compare the data from your experiment with a theoretical prediction. You can do this by calculating pairs of coordinates from the theoretical relationship between the variables, plotting these theoretical points on the graph and drawing a straight line or a smooth curve through them. Be careful that the theoretical points are easily distinguished from the experimental data.

For the sake of completeness and for easy reference, we list below a number of other guidelines that we will discuss in more detail later in this book.

(i) Use uncertainty bars to represent the range of uncertainty of the points plotted If you have been able to estimate the uncertainties associated with your data, then you should represent these by horizontal and vertical bars attached to the plotted points. Uncertainty bars, or error bars as they are often called, are discussed in Section 8.2.

(j) The best-fit straight line or curve should go through most of the uncertainty bars Also, there should be roughly the same number of points above the best-fit line as below it (Section 8.2).

(k) Whenever possible, plot the data in such a way that it can be represented by a straight-line graph The gradient and intercept of the line can be deduced from a straight-line graph (Section 8.3), and these values allow you to write down an equation relating the plotted variables. It is much easier to find the best straight line to fit data than to find the best curve, since you can fit a straight line by eye using a transparent ruler. When drawing the best line, think carefully about whether the line should go through the origin. Don't *force* the line to pass through the origin if that is not consistent with your data.

8.2 Uncertainty bars

When plotting a graph, you should use *uncertainty bars* whenever possible to indicate the uncertainties associated with your experimental measurements. Both horizontal and vertical uncertainty bars should be plotted, with one set omitted only if the associated uncertainty is too small to show up on the graph.

For example, suppose you measured the extension e of a wire when various masses m were hung from it, and found that a 5 kg mass produced an extension of 0.2 mm and 10 kg produced an extension of 0.5 mm. In addition, suppose you estimated that the uncertainty in measuring the extension was ± 0.05 mm and the uncertainty in the masses was ± 0.6 kg. The correct way to plot uncertainty bars for these results is shown in Figure 8.4. The circled points indicate the measured values. The uncertainty in each extension is indicated by a vertical uncertainty bar, which extends 0.05 above and 0.05 below the circled point, whilst the mass uncertainties are indicated by horizontal bars, which extend 0.6 on either side of the plotted mass value. However, suppose that the uncertainty in the masses had been ± 0.01 kg, which would be a much more realistic value for the uncertainty in the mass. Then the horizontal uncertainty bars would have been omitted because they would only be 1/20 of a small division, which is too small to plot on the graph in Figure 8.4.

Plotting uncertainty bars is slightly more complicated if you are not plotting a measured quantity directly, but some function of it, such as A^2, $\sin A$ or $\log A$. In such cases, you will need to use some of the rules that were quoted in Table 6.1. For example, if a power is involved, you can use the rule in Equation 6.6:

$$\text{percentage uncertainty in } A^n = n \times \text{percentage uncertainty in } A.$$

Thus if the uncertainty in A is $\pm 5\%$, the uncertainty in A^2 is $\pm 10\%$.

For other functions $f(A)$, the most straightforward procedure is to plot the maximum estimated value $f(A + \delta A)$ and the minimum estimated value $f(A - \delta A)$ and draw the uncertainty bar to join them. For example, if $A = (2.0 \pm 0.1)$, and you want to plot $\log_{10}A$ with its error bar, then you would plot a point at $\log_{10} 2.0$ (= 0.30), and draw

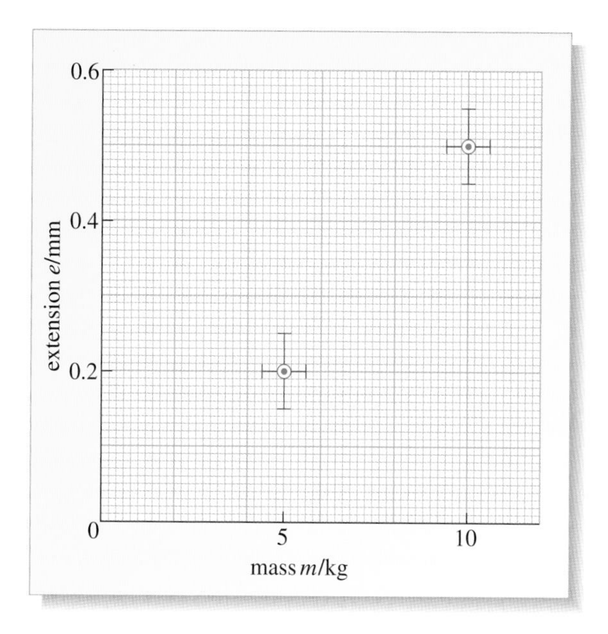

Figure 8.4 Use of vertical and horizontal bars to indicate uncertainties in data. The horizontal bars indicate that there is an uncertainty of ±0.6 kg in the mass measurements, and the vertical bars indicate an uncertainty of ±0.05 mm in the extension measurements.

an uncertainty bar to span the range from $\log_{10} 2.1$ (= 0.32) to $\log_{10} 1.9$ (= 0.28). Note that the uncertainty bars will vary from point to point if $f(A)$ is not a linear function (a straight line), even if the uncertainties in the original measurements of A are all the same.

Plotting uncertainty bars on a graph serves a number of useful purposes. The relationship between the plotted quantities can often be represented by a line that is either straight or a smooth curve, and we would then expect the data points to be scattered fairly equally on either side of that line. If the uncertainty bars represent the standard deviation of the plotted quantities, then we would expect the line to pass through about 2/3 of the bars. If the measured values deviate from the line by much more than the uncertainty bars, as shown in Figure 8.5a, then either we have underestimated the uncertainties, or the assumption that this line describes the results is not valid. On the other hand, if the line passes close to the centre of all of the uncertainty bars, as in Figure 8.5b, then it is likely that we have over-estimated the uncertainties. An alternative explanation in this latter case could be that the dominant contribution to the uncertainty bars is from a systematic uncertainty, so that the 'true' curve could be similar to the curve drawn in Figure 8.5b but shifted upwards or downwards on the graph within the range of the uncertainty bars.

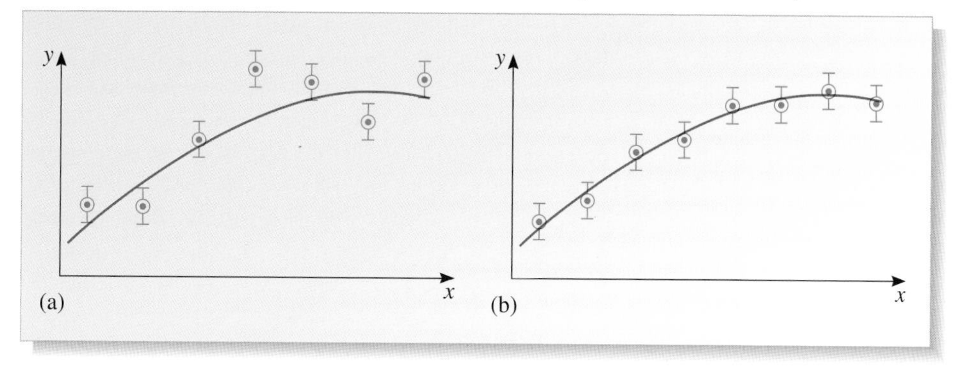

Figure 8.5 (a) Have the uncertainties in the data been underestimated? (b) Have the uncertainties been overestimated?

Uncertainty bars are also very helpful in identifying mistakes in measurements or in plotting the points. For example, if a point deviates from the general trend of the other data points by significantly more than the size of the uncertainty bars, it would be reasonable to be suspicious of this 'odd' measurement. In cases like this, the plotting of the anomalous point on the graph should be checked, and any calculations made to derive the plotted values should be checked as well. If these checks don't show up a mistake, then the measurements that gave rise to the suspect point should be repeated. In some cases, of course, repeating the measurements is just not possible, and one is left with the difficult decision about whether to ignore the point or not. No hard and fast rule can be made about this, but you should not discard data lightly. Bear in mind that what appears to be an anomalous measurement may actually indicate a real (and possibly undiscovered) effect!

Question 8.2 Use Figure 8.6 to plot the following three data points, together with their uncertainty bars.

(a) $V = (2.5 \pm 0.1)$ volts, $i = (1.5 \pm 0.3)$ amps.

(b) $V = 2.9$ volts $\pm 5\%$, $i = 4.1$ amps $\pm 10\%$.

(c) $V = (3.60 \pm 0.01)$ volts, $i = (2.5 \pm 0.5)$ amps. ■

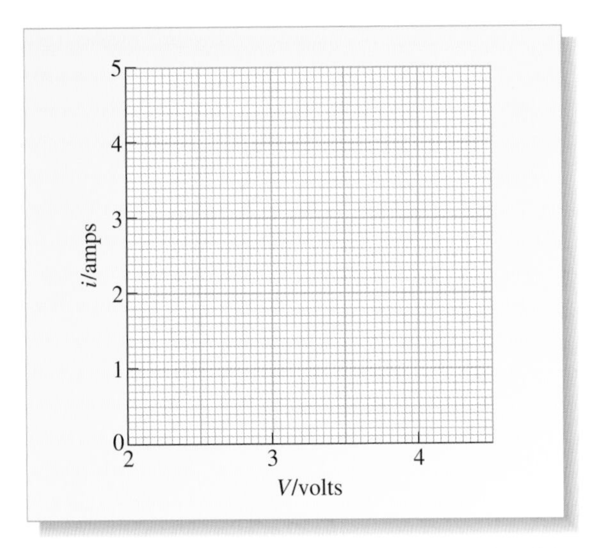

Figure 8.6 Graph paper for use with Question 8.2.

Question 8.3 In Question 8.1 at the end of Section 8 you were asked to criticize the graph plotted in Figure 8.2. After studying Sections 8.1 and 8.2 you should be able to do this more effectively. So look again at Figure 8.2, and list up to ten ways in which the student who plotted this graph departed from the guidelines in Section 8.1, and then compare your list with the list in the answer to this question. ■

8.3 Straight-line graphs: gradients, intercepts and their uncertainties

Physicists frequently plot their data in such a way that they can be represented by a straight line. One reason for this is that deviations from a straight line are much easier to see than deviations from a curve. However, just as important, it is easy to deduce the equation that represents a straight line that you have drawn on a graph. This equation expresses the relationship between the experimental quantities, and it may be possible to compare the values of the numerical constants in the equation with those predicted by a theoretical relationship.

The equation of any straight line on a graph of y versus x can be written as

$$y = mx + c. \tag{8.1}$$

The significance of the constants m and c in this equation is illustrated in Figure 8.7a. The constant m is the **gradient** of the line:

$$\text{gradient } m = \frac{\text{rise}}{\text{run}} = \frac{\Delta y}{\Delta x} \tag{8.2}$$

and c is the **intercept** with the y-axis, i.e. the value of y when $x = 0$. Thus

$$\begin{pmatrix}\text{value plotted on}\\ \text{vertical axis}\end{pmatrix} = \text{gradient} \times \begin{pmatrix}\text{value plotted on}\\ \text{horizontal axis}\end{pmatrix} + \begin{pmatrix}\text{intercept with}\\ \text{vertical axis}\end{pmatrix}. \tag{8.3}$$

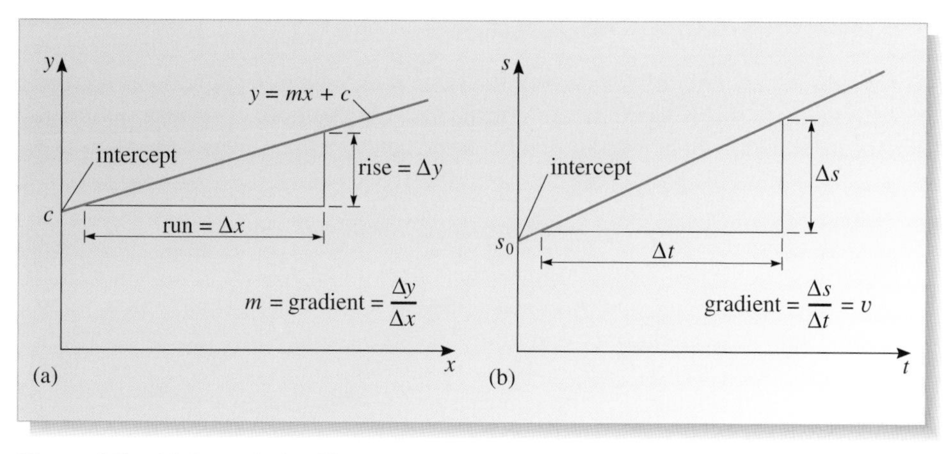

Figure 8.7 (a) A graph that illustrates the meaning of the constants m and c in the general equation of a straight line, $y = mx + c$. (b) A straight-line graph that represents the motion of a car at constant speed v.

Figure 8.7b shows a graph of distance s versus time t and, by analogy with Equations 8.1 and 8.3, the equation for the straight line plotted there is:

$$s = (\text{gradient} \times t) + (\text{intercept with } s\text{-axis}).$$

The gradient of this line is given by

$$\text{gradient} = \frac{\text{rise}}{\text{run}} = \frac{\Delta s}{\Delta t}$$

and this is equal to the average speed v of the object. The intercept with the s-axis represents the position s_0 of the object at $t = 0$.

Now consider an experiment in which the distance s travelled by an object is measured at various times t. A graph of the experimental data is shown in Figure 8.8.

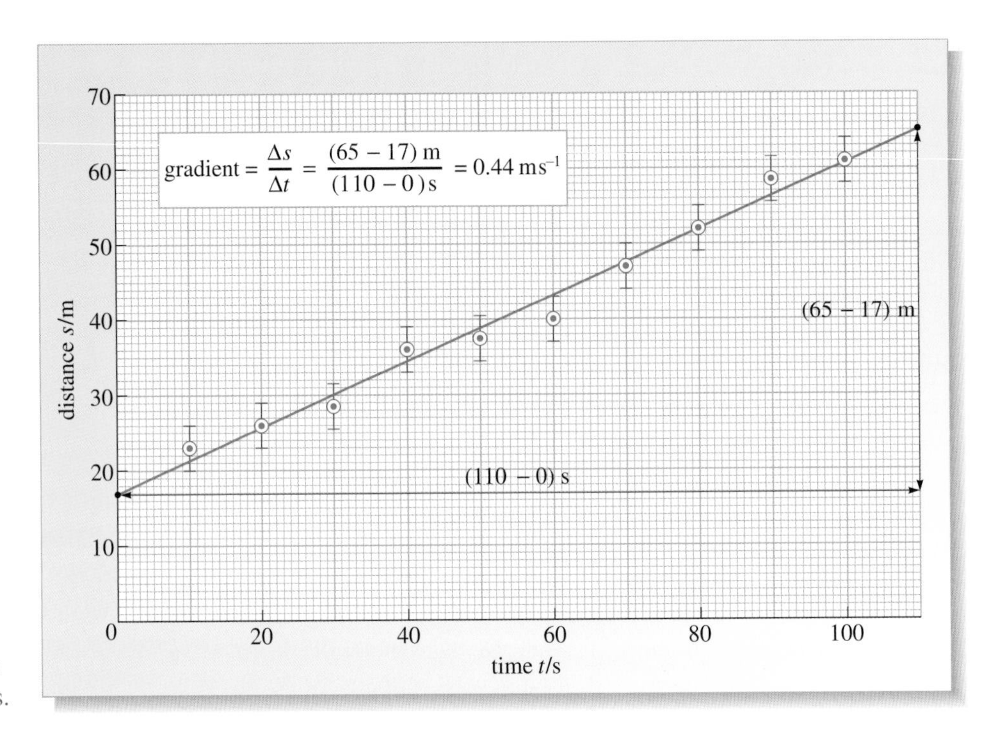

Figure 8.8 A graph showing measured values of the distance an object has travelled at various times.

- What can you deduce, from the graph in Figure 8.8, about the uncertainties in the measurements of distance and time?

❍ The vertical uncertainty bars are all the same size, and correspond to an uncertainty in the distance measurements of ±3 m. No horizontal uncertainty bars are shown, which implies that the uncertainty in the timing was less than one division on the graph paper, i.e. less than ±1 s.

- Are the data consistent with the object travelling at constant speed?

❍ Figure 8.8 shows that a straight line can be drawn that passes through almost all of the uncertainty bars, and this means that the data are consistent with a linear relationship between distance and time. The data are therefore consistent with motion at constant speed, since a linear relationship between distance and time (i.e. the position changes by the same amount for equal increments of time) is precisely what is meant by an object travelling at constant speed. ■

This is an important qualitative deduction that can be made from the graph. Of course, if we had been unable to draw a line that passed through most of the uncertainty bars, then we would have concluded either that the motion was not represented by a linear relationship (i.e. the speed was not constant), or that the uncertainty in some of the measurements was greater than indicated. Now let's make some quantitative deductions from the straight-line graph in Figure 8.8.

The gradient of the straight line in Figure 8.8 is our best estimate of the speed of the object. To work out the gradient of the line, we select any pair of points *that lie on the straight line.* (Note that the straight line effectively averages out the uncertainties in individual data points, so we always work with values on the line, rather than with values from the original data, which may well not be on the line). The rise Δs is then the difference between the s-values of the two selected points, and the run Δt is the difference between the t-values of these points, as shown in Figure 8.8. Thus

$$\text{gradient} = \frac{(65-17)\,\text{m}}{(110-0)\,\text{s}} = \frac{48}{110}\,\text{m}\,\text{s}^{-1} = 0.44\,\text{m}\,\text{s}^{-1}.$$

Note that the gradient does *not* depend on which pair of points on the line you use to calculate it. However, the coordinates of the points can be estimated from the graph with only limited precision. The best practice, therefore, is to choose two points on the line that are as widely separated as possible. The uncertainties in reading the coordinates will then be much smaller fractions of the differences between the coordinates than if the two points were close together.

The straight line drawn in Figure 8.8 is our choice of the 'best fit' to the data. It was drawn so that it passes as close as possible to the data points and the points above the line are balanced by other points below the line. Remember that we expect the line to pass through about two-thirds of the uncertainty bars. However, many other lines with different gradients could also be drawn to pass through about two-thirds of the uncertainty bars. In order to obtain an estimate of the *uncertainty in the gradient*, we can draw the line that has the *maximum* possible gradient consistent with the data, and similarly draw the line that has the *minimum* possible gradient consistent with the data. These lines are shown in Figure 8.9, and their gradients are $0.52\,\text{m s}^{-1}$ and $0.35\,\text{m s}^{-1}$, respectively. These values differ from the gradient of the 'best' straight line by $0.08\,\text{m s}^{-1}$ and $0.09\,\text{m s}^{-1}$. Taking the average of these ($0.085\,\text{m s}^{-1}$) and rounding it to one significant figure, we can quote the value of the gradient as $(0.44 \pm 0.09)\,\text{m s}^{-1}$.

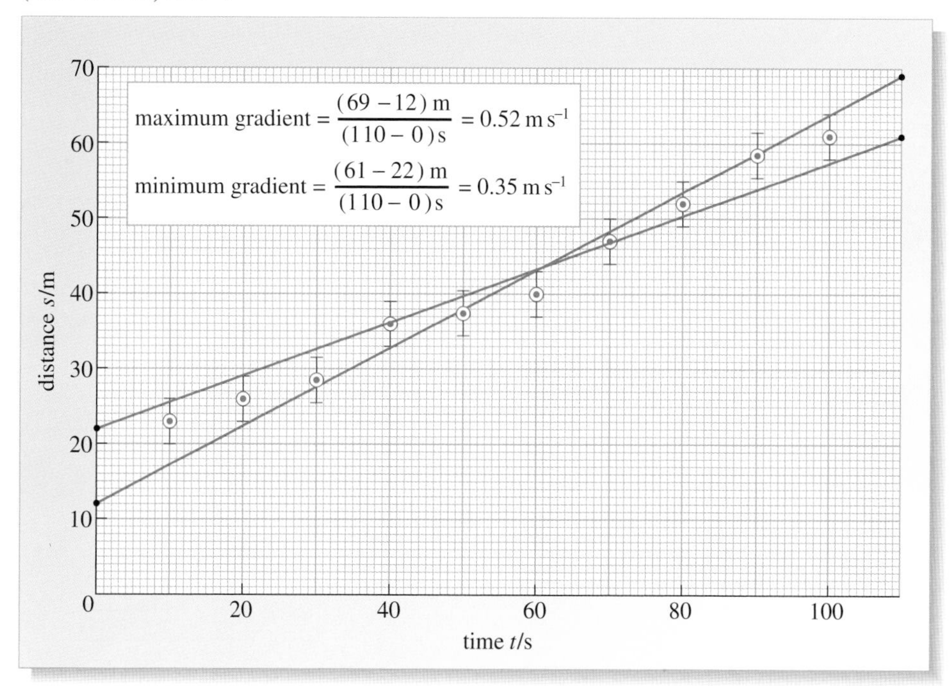

Figure 8.9 The uncertainty in the gradient is estimated by drawing the steepest and shallowest lines that still pass through about two-thirds of the uncertainty bars, and then measuring the gradients of these lines. (These lines would normally be drawn on the same graph as the best fit line.)

The other quantity that specifies the position of a straight line on a graph is its intercept with the s-axis, and we have called this s_0, the value of s at $t = 0$. For the straight line shown in Figure 8.8, the intercept is at $s = 17\,\text{m}$ and, since this is determined from the 'best' straight line, it is the best estimate of the intercept. The upper and lower limits for the intercepts are found, as you might expect, from the intercepts of the lines with minimum and maximum gradients shown in Figure 8.9. These intercepts are 22 m and 12 m respectively, and they differ from the best intercept by +5 m and −5 m, respectively. The experimentally determined intercept can therefore be quoted as $(17 \pm 5)\,\text{m}$.

We can use the values for the gradients and intercepts that we have determined from the graphs in Figures 8.8 and 8.9 to write down an equation for the relationship between position and time in this experiment:

$$s = (0.44 \pm 0.09)\,\mathrm{m\,s^{-1}} \times t \; + \; (17 \pm 5)\,\mathrm{m}.$$

Box 8.1 describes an alternative way to determine the gradient of a straight line and its uncertainty.

Box 8.1 Gradient measurement by pairing points

Sometimes the uncertainty bars are too small to show on the graph, and a straight line can be drawn that passes very close to all of the plotted points. It is straightforward to determine the gradient of the line shown in Figure 8.10, but it is very difficult to draw lines of maximum and minimum gradient that are clearly separate from the best line. This means that the uncertainty in the gradient cannot be determined using the graphical method that was described above.

We have emphasized that all measurements have some associated uncertainty, so we need an alternative method of assessing the uncertainty in the gradient in this situation. One method that can be used is the so-called *pairing points* method, and we will illustrate this method using the data in the first and third columns of Table 8.3, which were used to plot the graph in Figure 8.10. Essentially the pairing points method involves calculating a series of values of the gradient from different pairs of data points. So we calculate a run $\Delta m = m_6 - m_1$ and a rise $\Delta e = e_6 - e_1$ from the coordinates of the first and the sixth measurements, and these values are shown in the second and fourth columns of the table. We can then calculate a value for the gradient $\Delta e/\Delta m$ from these values of Δe and Δm, and this value is shown in the fifth column. This procedure is then repeated for the second and seventh measurements, third and eighth, and so on. Thus from 10 measurements we get 10/2 = 5 values for the gradient, and the best estimate of the gradient is the mean of these five values. The uncertainty in the gradient can be estimated from the spread of the five values, or better still by calculating the uncertainty of the mean value (Section 6.1).

● Why is it better to take differences between measurements 1 and 6, between 2 and 7, etc., rather than between 1 and 2, between 3 and 4, etc?

❍ The reason is the same as for using widely spaced points to measure the gradient of a line on a graph — the larger the separation of the points, the smaller are the fractional uncertainties in the differences between their coordinates. ■

The pairing points method is not restricted to data that lie very close to a straight line. It can be used when the uncertainties in the data are much larger, and it will produce a more objective result than drawing lines of maximum and minimum gradient (a rather subjective process) and calculating their gradients. However, the pairs of points should be fairly evenly spaced; if they are not, then more weight would need to be given to the gradients calculated from the more-widely-spaced pairs of points.

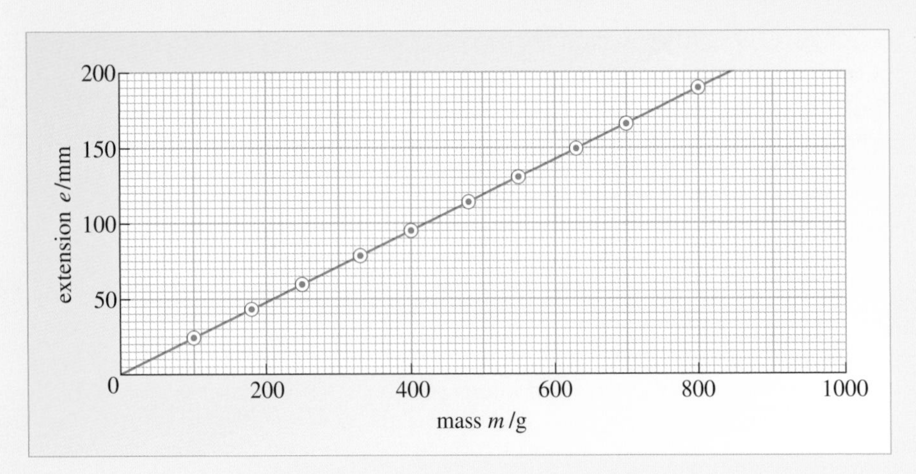

Figure 8.10 Results of an experiment in which the extension e of a spring was measured for ten different values of the mass m suspended from its end. The uncertainties in the measurements are too small to show on this graph. How do we determine the uncertainty in the gradient of the line?

mass m/g	Δm/g	extension e/mm	Δe/mm	$(\Delta e/\Delta m)$/(mm g^{-1})
100		24.0		
180		43.0		
250	380	59.0	89.5	0.2355
330	370	77.5	88.0	0.2378
400	380	96.0	91.0	0.2395
480	370	113.5	89.0	0.2405
550	400	131.5	93.5	0.2338
630		150.0		
700		166.5		mean = 0.2374
800		189.5		$s_m = \pm 0.0013$

Table 8.3 The first and third columns show the mass m and extension e used to plot the graph in Figure 8.10. The second column shows the differences Δm between masses in rows 1 and 6, rows 2 and 7, etc. The fourth column shows differences Δe between extensions in rows 1 and 6, rows 2 and 7, etc. Values of the gradient $\Delta e/\Delta m$ of the line are determined from corresponding values of Δe and Δm and these appear in the fifth column. (Note that colour, braces and arrows have been used here to clarify how the data is analysed; you are not expected to produce colourful tables like this!)

Question 8.4 Figure 8.11 shows a graph of the pressure P of a fixed volume of gas versus its temperature θ.

(a) Draw on the graph your estimate of the best-fit straight line for this data, and determine the gradient of this line and its intercept with the pressure axis.

(b) What are the uncertainties in the gradient and the intercept?

(c) Use your results from (a) and (b) to write down an equation that represents the result of this experiment. Your equation should include numerical values of the constants. ■

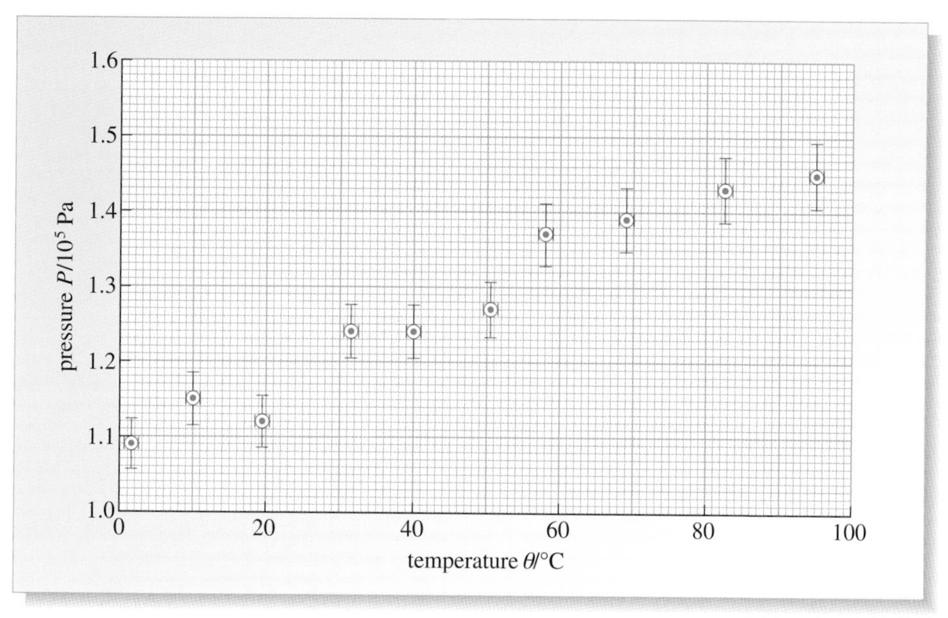

Figure 8.11 Experimental results for the dependence of the pressure P of a fixed volume of helium gas on temperature θ. For use with Question 8.4.

8.4 Transforming curves into straight lines

You have seen that it is straightforward to deduce an equation relating two variables when their relationship can be represented by a straight-line graph. Can the same thing be done with curved graphs? Unfortunately, the answer is no; it cannot be done directly. However, it is often possible to plot *functions* of the original variables (e.g. s^2, $\sin\theta$, $\log_e N$, etc.) so that the points on the graph are represented by a straight line. It is then possible to deduce the equation for this linear relationship from the graph, and hence deduce the relationship between the original variables. We will now give a couple of examples of how this could be done in practice.

First, suppose that we measured the area A and radius r of a set of circles. Plotting A versus r will certainly not produce a straight line: it produces a parabola, as shown in Figure 8.12a. However, if A is plotted against r^2, then the resulting graph *is* a straight line, as shown in Figure 8.12b, with a gradient that appears to be about 3.1 and intercept zero.

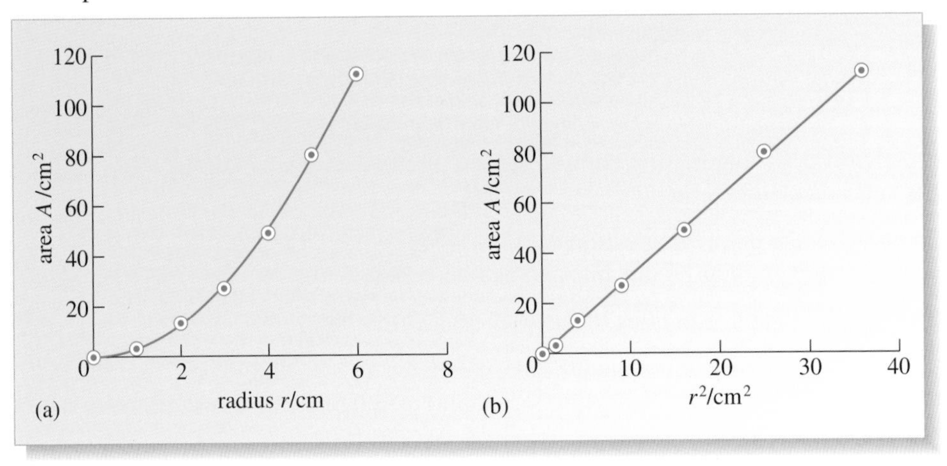

Figure 8.12 (a) Measurements of the area A of circles of radius r. The relationship is parabolic. (b) The same data as in (a), but plotted as area A versus r^2. This graph demonstrates that A is linearly related to r^2.

It is instructive to relate the graph in Figure 8.12b to the general form of the equation of a straight line

$$y = mx + c, \tag{8.1}$$

where y is the quantity plotted on the vertical axis and x is the quantity plotted on the horizontal axis. Area A plotted vertically is analogous to y, and r^2 plotted horizontally is analogous to x. The gradient $m = 3.1$, and the intercept c = zero, so there is no constant term. The equation of this line is therefore

$$A = 3.1r^2,$$

which is consistent with a well-known result from geometry, $A = \pi r^2$.

As a second example, suppose that we had reason to suspect that the relationship between two measured quantities, z and θ, is represented by the equation

$$z^2 = a\sin\theta - b,$$

where a and b are constants. Comparing this equation with our general equation for a straight line (Equation 8.1), we can see that z^2 is analogous to y and $\sin\theta$ is analogous to x. We could confirm or disprove this relationship by plotting a graph of z^2 versus $\sin\theta$. If the measurements were consistent with a relationship of this form, then we should be able to draw a straight line through the data points. The gradient of this line would be equal to a, and the intercept with the z^2-axis would be at $-b$.

We recommend that whenever possible, you should plot your data in a way that will give you a straight line. Deviations from linearity are easy to see, so a straight-line graph soon shows up any deficiencies in the data.

Question 8.5 Each of the examples below specifies two variables that were measured in an experiment, and a relationship between them that the experimenter is seeking to verify. In each case, decide what graph you would plot to obtain a straight line that confirmed the validity of the relationship.

(a) Variables: pressure P and volume V of a fixed quantity (n moles) of gas at a fixed temperature T. Relationship: $PV = nRT$.

(b) Variables: power P and current I for a fixed resistance R. Relationship: $P = I^2R$.

(c) Variables: pressure P and height z for an isothermal (i.e. constant temperature) atmosphere. Relationship: $P = P_0\, e^{-z/\lambda}$. ■

9 Using calculators and computers to analyse and display experimental results

Programmable graphical calculators and computers can often greatly simplify the analysis and display of experimental data. They can be used to calculate the mean and standard deviation of a set of measurements, to plot a graph of data, to determine the best-fit straight line or curve for your data, and much more besides.

It is not appropriate to give specific guidance here on how you can carry out these various operations, because the detailed procedures depend on the particular combination of hardware and software that are available to you. However, we will indicate some of the possible applications, and you can investigate for yourself how to implement them with your calculator or computer.

9.1 Using a computer spreadsheet program

Spreadsheet programs are very powerful tools for the physicist, and Figure 9.1 illustrates a few of the ways in which they can be used to display and analyse experimental data. In the example shown there, the initial data was obtained by measuring the heights and radii of ten cylinders.

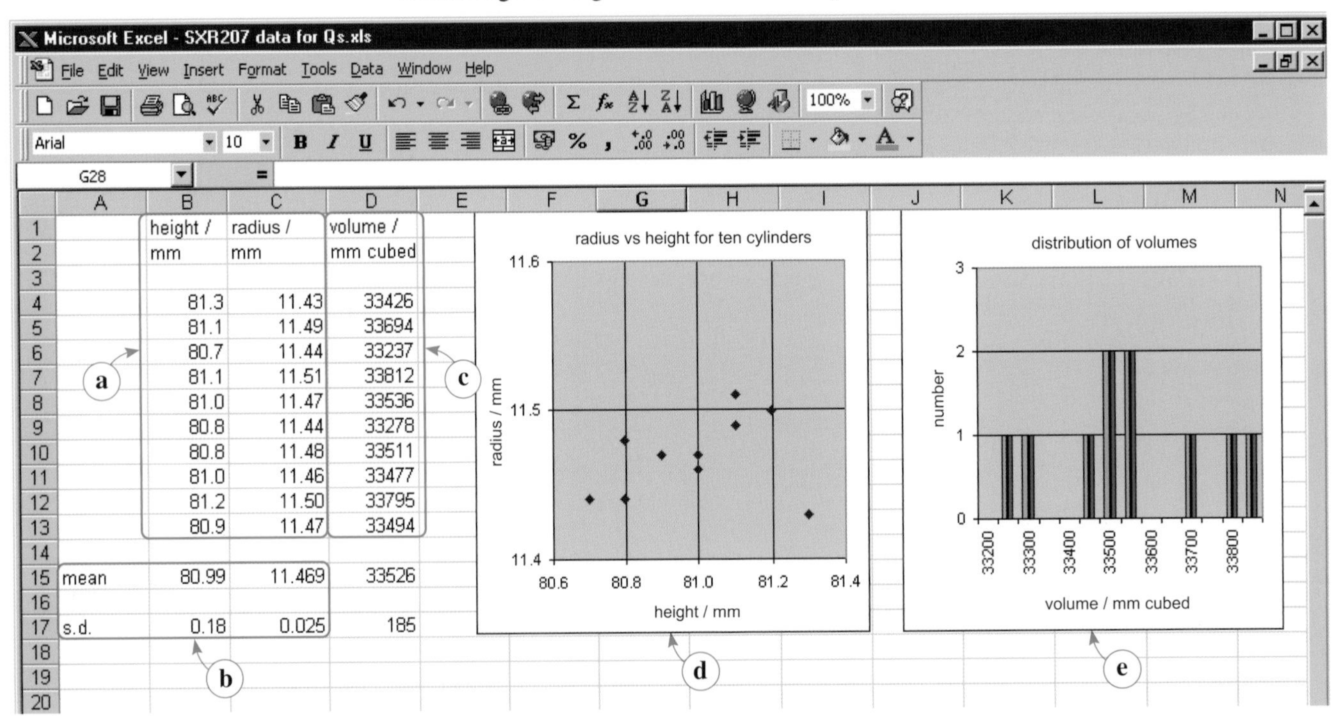

	A	B	C	D
1		height /	radius /	volume /
2		mm	mm	mm cubed
3				
4		81.3	11.43	33426
5		81.1	11.49	33694
6		80.7	11.44	33237
7		81.1	11.51	33812
8		81.0	11.47	33536
9		80.8	11.44	33278
10		80.8	11.48	33511
11		81.0	11.46	33477
12		81.2	11.50	33795
13		80.9	11.47	33494
14				
15	mean	80.99	11.469	33526
16				
17	s.d.	0.18	0.025	185

Figure 9.1 An example of how a spreadsheet can be used for data analysis and display. The areas of the spreadsheet labelled (**a**), (**b**), (**c**), etc. are described in the text.

(a) Produce a table of data You can enter your measurements into the rows and columns of a ready-made table, as shown in area (**a**) of Figure 9.1. Each number is keyed into a separate box, called a *cell*. Columns and/or rows can be labelled to indicate the quantities tabulated, and their units. In the example in Figure 9.1, ten pairs of values of cylinder height and cylinder radius have been entered.

(b) Calculate the mean and standard deviation of a set of data You can ask the computer to calculate the mean of the values in a set of cells and enter this in another cell. Similarly, you can ask the computer to calculate the standard deviation of the values in a set of cells. In Figure 9.1, area (**b**), the computer has calculated the means and standard deviations for both the height and the radius. It only requires about a half-dozen mouse clicks to calculate each of these values, irrespective of how large the data set. This means that once you have familiarized yourself with the procedure, you can save yourself a lot of time when analysing data this way.

Most scientific calculators have a facility for calculating the mean and standard deviation of a series of numbers: you simply key in the numbers, press the 'mean' key and note the result, and then press the 'standard deviation' key and note the result. Again, this is much easier than doing the standard deviation calculation by hand in the way shown in Table 5.1.

(c) Calculate functions of values in one or more cell In area (**c**) of Figure 9.1 we have calculated the cylinder volume as $\pi \times \text{height} \times (\text{radius})^2$. The computer was instructed first to evaluate the volume corresponding to the first pair of data values, and this instruction was then copied to all of the other volume cells in order to complete the data in the volume column. Again there are big savings of time when large data sets are used.

(d) Plot a graph The computer can plot a graph of data from two columns (or two rows), and in area (**d**) in Figure 9.1 a graph of radius versus height has been plotted. You can choose the style of the graph (e.g. displaying data points only, or displaying a histogram). Normally the computer will automatically choose appropriate scales to display the data, but you can make your own choices of scale if you wish. Uncertainty (error) bars can be displayed, though in many programs the uncertainty bars have to be either the same magnitude for each point or the same percentage of each value plotted.

(e) Produce a histogram showing the distribution of measured values of a quantity In area (**e**) of Figure 9.1 the distribution of the measured values of the cylinder volume has been displayed.

Figure 9.2 shows a second example of the use of a spreadsheet for data analysis, this time in an experiment to measure the radioactive decay constant of a short-lived isotope.

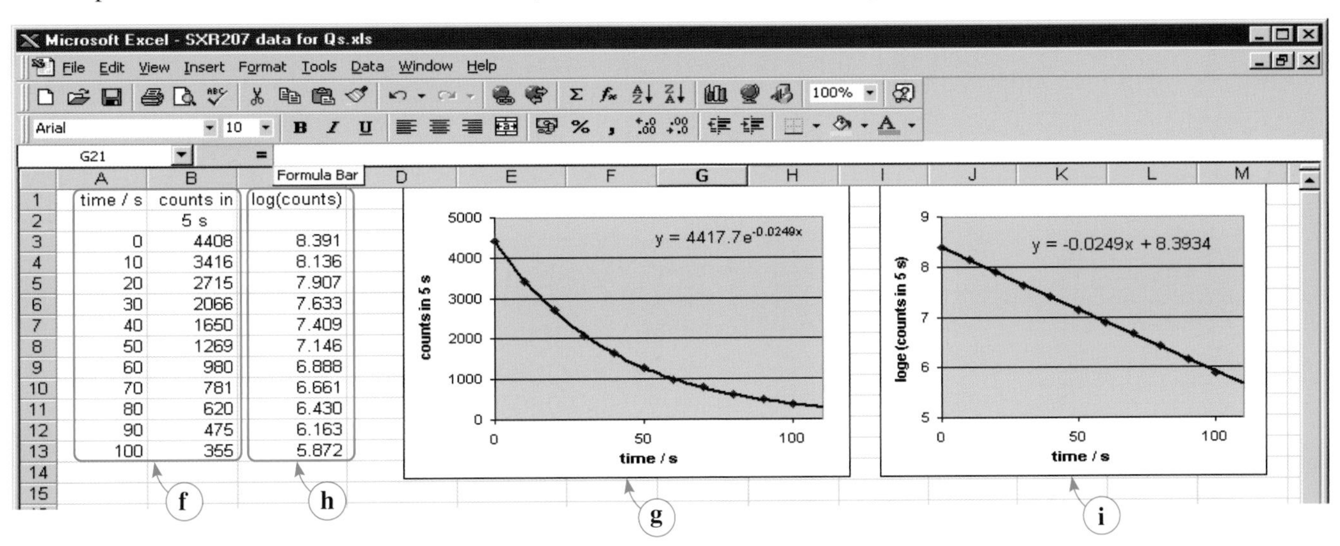

time / s	counts in 5 s	log(counts)
0	4408	8.391
10	3416	8.136
20	2715	7.907
30	2066	7.633
40	1650	7.409
50	1269	7.146
60	980	6.888
70	781	6.661
80	620	6.430
90	475	6.163
100	355	5.872

Figure 9.2 The use of a spreadsheet in a radioactivity experiment. The areas of the spreadsheet labelled (**f**), (**g**), etc. are described in the text.

(f) Data tabulation The first column of the spreadsheet in area (**f**) of Figure 9.2 shows the times at which data were recorded, and the second column shows the number of counts measured by a Geiger counter in 5-second intervals ending at these times.

(g) Plot a graph and fit a curve to the plotted data In area (**g**) of Figure 9.2 a graph of counts versus time has been plotted. The computer has fitted an exponential curve to the data, and has displayed the equation of the fitted curve. The constant 0.0249 in the exponent of the exponential is the *decay constant* for this isotope and is equal to 0.6932/(half-life). Note a limitation of this spreadsheet program: it does not display the units of the constants in the fitted equation. When you transcribe equations displayed by the computer, you will therefore have to work out the appropriate units for the constants, and insert them into the equation.

(h) Calculate a function of data values in a column If a column contains values of a quantity x, you can produce additional columns containing any function of x, such as $3x^2 + 5$, $(\sin x)/x$, or $\exp(-mgx/kT)$. It is therefore very easy to transform your data so that you can plot it in a way that produces a straight line. The graph in area (**g**) indicates that there is an exponential relationship between counts and time, which means that $\log_e$(counts) is linearly related to time. In Figure 9.2, the values of $\log_e$(counts) shown in area (**h**) have been calculated from the values of 'counts' shown in the second column of area (**f**).

(i) Fit a straight line to the transformed data It is possible to plot graphs of the data in the new column, and the graph in area (**i**) shows $\log_e$(counts) plotted versus time. The computer has drawn the best-fit straight line for the plotted data points, and has displayed the equation of this straight line. Values of the uncertainties in the gradient and intercept of the line are not normally displayed. Note that the value of the gradient of the straight-line graph of $\log_e$(counts) versus time has the same value as the constant in the exponent of the exponential curve in area (**g**), as would be expected.

As well as fitting straight lines or exponential curves to data, it is also possible to fit curves described by various other functions, and these functions include polynomials and logarithmic functions. Fitting a straight line or a curve to data normally uses a statistical procedure known as the *least-squares method*, and this is discussed in Box 9.1.

Box 9.1 The least-squares method of curve fitting

We will illustrate the least-squares method by considering the fitting of a straight line to the data plotted in Figure 9.3. A variety of straight lines, represented by $y = mx + c$, could be drawn on the graph, and we want to find the values of m and c that produce the line that is the 'best fit' to the data. For simplicity, we will assume that the uncertainties in y are the same for all data points, and the uncertainties in x are negligible.

What do we mean by 'best fit'? Clearly, we want the line to be positioned so that it passes as close to the data points as possible. So we want to find the values of m and c that in some sense minimize the lengths of the short lines shown connecting the data points with the straight line in Figure 9.3. Now if the coordinates of the ith data point are (x_i, y_i), then the y-coordinate of the straight line when $x = x_i$ must be $(mx_i + c)$. Thus the vertical separation between the ith data point and the straight line is just $y_i - (mx_i + c)$, and it is these separations that are represented by the short lines in Figure 9.3.

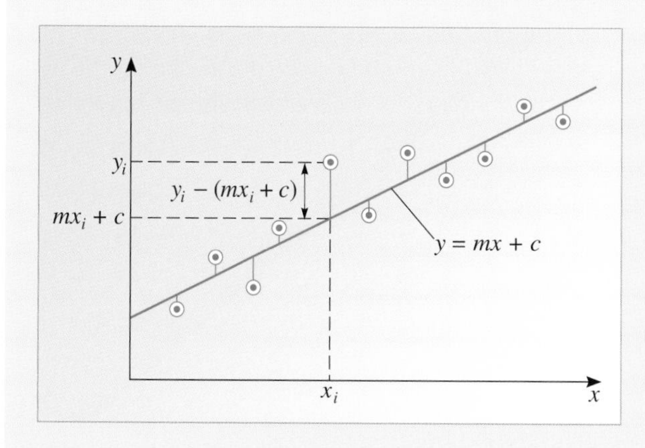

Figure 9.3 A set of data points, and a straight line drawn to represent the data. The vertical lines between the data points and the line represent the deviations of the data points from the line.

Now we can't find the best-fit straight line by simply minimizing the sum of all of the separations $y_i - (mx_i + c)$, since large positive separations could be cancelled by large negative separations. Instead we find the best line by minimizing the sum of the *squares* of the separations (which must all be positive), i.e. we minimize

$$\sum_{i=1}^{n}(y_i - mx_i + c)^2 = (y_1 - mx_1 + c)^2 + (y_2 - mx_2 + c)^2 + (y_3 - mx_3 + c)^2 + \ldots$$

This is why the method is known as the **least-squares method**.

Standard techniques of calculus can be used to evaluate the conditions for this summation to have its minimum value. They lead to explicit expressions for the gradient m and the intercept c that appear in the equation of a straight line. We will not reproduce the expressions for m and c here, since the computer or calculator that you use to implement the least-squares method will display the results for m and c automatically.

The least-squares method is not limited to fitting a straight line to data, but can be used to fit a variety of other functions, such as:

- a power law, of the form ax^b,
- a polynomial function; for example, $ax^3 + bx^2 + cx + d$; programs generally allow a choice of the highest power included in the function;
- an exponential function; for example, ae^{bx},
- a logarithmic function of the form $a \log_e x + b$.

For each of these functions, the computer program can calculate the values of the constants (a, b, c, d) that minimize the sum of the squares of the separations of the data points from the curve. In many experiments, you will base your choice of the type of function to fit to the data on a theoretical relationship between the variables. In other cases, you may be trying to identify the (unknown) functional relationship between the measured variables. You then need to compare the best curves computed for different types of function with the data points to see which curve is the best representation of the data.

Using the least-squares method on a computer to find the best-fit straight line for a data set is far easier than plotting a graph by hand and then calculating gradients and intercepts. However, it may not be as easy to 'plot as you go' using a computer. You may therefore need to plot a rough graph while taking measurements, and then use a computer for a least-squares fit when all of the data has been collected.

If you have access to a computer with a spreadsheet program or a calculator with statistical analysis functions, then you might like to use it to analyse the data in Questions 9.1 and 9.2. The answers are provided at the end of the book, but we will not be able to give specific advice about the method of data analysis because of the variety of software available.

Table 9.1 The temperature dependence of the resistance of a coil of copper wire between 0 °C and 35.5 °C.

Temperature θ /°C	Resistance R /ohms
0.0	27.6
5.5	28.1
10.0	28.9
15.0	29.5
19.5	29.7
24.5	30.1
30.0	31.0
35.5	31.8

Question 9.1 Table 9.1 shows data from an experiment in which a student measured the dependence of the resistance of a coil of copper wire on temperature.

(a) Use your computer or calculator to display a graph of this data.

(b) Compute the equation of the best-fit straight line.

Question 9.2 The diameter of a glass capillary tube was measured ten times with a microscope, and the values obtained (in μm) are shown below.

786, 789, 787, 792, 785, 781, 787, 790, 785, 784.

Use your computer or calculator to calculate (a) the mean, (b) the standard deviation, and (c) the uncertainty of the mean for these measurements. ■

10 Communicating your results

Scientists need to be able to communicate their ideas and results effectively. There are many examples in the history of science where scientists have made significant discoveries, but not publicized them. For example, Henry Cavendish was an eighteenth-century British scientist, who carried out extensive experiments on electrical phenomena. However, he rarely took the trouble to write up his findings, so that for many years other people continued to work on problems that he had already solved. He discovered that the current I through a resistor is proportional to the voltage V applied across it. Fifty years later Ohm made the same discovery. Yet, this relationship is now known as Ohm's law, because it was Ohm who made his discovery known to others.

If communication of scientific results was important in the eighteenth century, it is perhaps even more essential at the beginning of the twenty-first century. A few centuries ago, science was only carried out by a small number of people, but now it is a huge enterprise, spread over academic and industrial institutions all round the world. The progress of science is very much a cooperative effort, with one group of scientists building on the discoveries of others, and then communicating their own results for other scientists to build on in turn. So research scientists publish papers describing their work in academic journals, and they attend conferences at which they give formal talks and have informal discussions about their latest findings.

Skill in the presentation of experimental results and the conclusions derived from them is something that every physicist should acquire, since the acceptance or rejection of their results and conclusions will usually be based on their written or oral reports. As a student, you will be able to develop and practise this skill by writing reports of experiments and possibly by giving oral presentations of your results to other students. If you fail to communicate clearly your results and their significance, your experimental work is unlikely to get the recognition that it may deserve.

10.1 Writing reports

There is a big difference between the way that you record information in your laboratory notebook, which is your personal record of your experimental work, and the way in which you present your final report. The main requirement of your notebook is that it should contain a record of all necessary information about the experiment in a form that will be accessible and intelligible to you in six months time, as well as immediately after completing the experiment. It should also allow another student or a colleague to repeat the experiment. A final report must contain all of the necessary information, but it must be presented in a way that is accessible to, and readily understandable by, the intended readers. Clarity, conciseness, and coherence are all at a premium. Any conclusions that you reach should be stated simply, with a clear indication of their limitations.

Here are a few guidelines for the presentation of experimental reports. They will give you an idea of what is likely to constitute an acceptable framework for a report, but you should not regard them as prescriptive.

(a) Give your report a title The title should be brief, but it needs to give the reader a clear idea of the subject of the report. If the aim of the experiment was to measure a particular quantity, to observe a particular phenomenon, or to confirm a theoretical prediction, then state this explicitly in the title. Novelists often choose titles that sound intriguing but give little idea of what their books are about; scientists should aim to provide a title that conveys relevant information.

(b) Start with an abstract The first component of your report should be an abstract that summarizes the work in a few sentences. It is usually best to write the abstract *after* you have completed the rest of the report, but it should appear at the beginning.

The important function of the abstract is to succinctly provide information that will allow a reader to decide whether they are interested in reading the report. It therefore needs to give the reader an overall picture of the general scope of the report and of the final results and main conclusions. Since it will be the first part — or perhaps the only part — of the report that a reader will see, the abstract needs to be intelligible without reading the main body of the report. In particular, you shouldn't use undefined terms or symbols with which the reader may not be familiar.

(c) Introduction In the introduction you should briefly set out the purpose of the experiment, and give a brief outline of how it was carried out. It may be appropriate to describe the theoretical background in order to put the experiment in context, but this may not always be necessary. If the purpose of the experiment is to verify a relationship or measure a specific quantity then you will need to explain what these are. Sometimes it may be appropriate to make references to textbooks or other documents where relationships are derived.

(d) Experimental method This section is the place where you describe how you carried out the experiment. You need to include details of the equipment used, any special precautions that you took to reduce uncertainties, any checks that you made and any problems encountered. It is often useful to include a labelled diagram showing how the equipment was set up, or showing some aspect of the experiment. Diagrams should each have a caption (e.g. Figure 1 The apparatus used to measure ...), and should be referred to at the appropriate place in the text. The length of this section will depend on the complexity of the experiment.

If you are writing a report of an experiment in which you have followed a procedure described in student notes, then there is no need to repeat all of the details that are in the notes. A brief summary and a reference to the notes will generally be enough.

(e) Results The results section is the place to present the measurements or observations that you have made. It is worth taking some trouble to organize your data into an easily digestible form, and this is often done most neatly using tables and graphs. As with diagrams, you should make sure that each of these has a caption (e.g. Table A Data for the extension of a copper wire for various loading masses; Figure 3 Graph showing extension versus load mass for a copper wire), and that it is referred to at the appropriate place(s) in the text. It is essential to label clearly the columns (and/or rows) in tables and the axes of graphs, and to include the correct units (Box 3.1).

This section should also contain the analysis of the data and the calculation of the result. It is not necessary to show all of the steps in the derivation of algebraic expressions that you use to analyse your data, unless you are using a non-standard method. Estimates of uncertainties in measurements should be included, together with an indication of how the individual uncertainties in measured values were combined to obtain the uncertainty in the final result.

(f) Discussion This is where you discuss how your experiment and the result fit in with other work and relevant theories; for example, is the result consistent with other published values? Make sure that you discuss any unexpected behaviour or results. You should also point out any assumptions or approximations that you have made, limitations in the experiment or the analysis, and you might suggest ways in which the experiment could be improved. You may also have suggestions for additional experiments or further investigations arising from the work that you have done.

(g) Conclusion This is usually the final part of the account, and it encapsulates in a few sentences the main outcomes of the experiment. It may include a numerical result — which should always be accompanied by an estimate of the uncertainty — or an equation that you have deduced or verified.

10.2 Good scientific writing

This is not the place to give detailed advice on how to write good English, but here are a few pointers that may be useful when you are producing reports of your experiments.

(a) Think about the structure of your report before you write it Dividing your report into the sections that we have just described is a good way to provide the main structure that is required. You then need to decide on the best order for the components of each section, and you may find it helpful to jot down an outline of the main topics that you need to include. This will help you to think about the links between the various topics and to fix on an order that seems logical. If there is a logical flow to the report, it will be much easier for you to write, but, more important, it will be much easier for the reader to follow!

(b) Avoid very long sentences It is possible to write clearly using long sentences, but it is much more difficult than writing short sentences. However, stringing together a series of very short sentences is likely to result in a rather boring prose style. Varying the length of your sentences will make your report more interesting to read.

(c) Divide long sections into paragraphs Start a new paragraph when you start a new topic or a different aspect of a topic. This makes your writing easier for the reader to follow. The first and last sentences in a paragraph often have the most impact on the reader, and some writers try to put their main points in these places.

(d) Active or passive voice? Opinion is divided over whether reports and scientific papers should be written in the active voice ('I measured the voltage ...', or 'We measured the voltage ...') or the passive voice ('The voltage was measured ...'). Your aim should be to make your written reports objective, but this doesn't mean you have to write in the passive voice. Most authors avoid the use of 'I' in scientific papers, but this is certainly not a rigid rule. Using 'we' is certainly acceptable, particularly when describing the actions or views of more than one person. Use of the passive voice to convey a sense of (unjustified) authority should be avoided. In particular, you should clearly distinguish between your own interpretations and those that are more widely accepted: thus writing about 'our interpretation of these results ...' or 'we suggest that these results show ...' is often preferable to 'the results show that ...'.

(e) Read your own writing critically If you find that you are having difficulty expressing something clearly, a possible approach to use is to ask yourself what you would *say* if you were telling somebody about this subject. Some people find it useful to read aloud to themselves what they have written. This helps to give them a feel for the flow of the words; usually if something is difficult for you to read to yourself when you know the intended meaning, then it will be difficult for your readers to follow. You can read to yourself as you complete a sentence, a paragraph, or a section. It is also very helpful to put aside what you have written for a couple of days, and then come back to it. Reading your written work through afresh will often make you aware of gaps in the logical flow of topics, or of points that are missing or unclear.

(f) Using a word processor can often be very helpful The advantage of a word processor is that it is very easy to change the wording, change the order of topics, change the paragraphing, and so on. Some people like to dash off a quick draft, and then polish this up, while others like to aim for something that is fairly polished first time round. Whatever your preference, a word processor gives you the freedom to modify and polish your draft bit by bit without having laboriously to rewrite the whole thing from scratch. It also enables you to check and correct spelling, and possibly your grammar too. However, one note of caution about using a word processor for mathematical equations. Producing clearly laid out equations with a word processor is much more difficult than doing it by hand. So unless you have a software package that enables you to lay out equations properly (and you know how to use it!), you should leave gaps for the equations, and insert them by hand after printing the report.

Answers and comments

Q3.1 You may have suggested some of the following improvements.

- Insert a date at the start.
- Information has been noted about the frequency generator, but information about the oscilloscope should also be recorded.
- A few more details about the experiment might have been helpful. For example, was a preliminary experiment done to locate the approximate position of the resonance peak? Were precautions taken to ensure that the current from the signal generator remained constant?
- No unit has been shown for the frequency column of the table; it is generally best to indicate the unit in the column headings of the table, and in this case it should be frequency/kHz.
- The unit is shown with each of the values in the second column, and while this is logically correct, including the unit in the column heading (i.e. voltage across LC/mV p-p) would simplify the table and would save writing out the unit with each value.
- Incorrect data should be crossed out neatly, rather than being obliterated, and the reason for the deletion should be noted.
- There are two notes in the table that the scale (on the oscilloscope) was changed, but no indication of what scales were used.
- There are a couple of cryptic comments (e.g. 'Connect leads right way round', 'tricky'); these may not be meaningful if they are read a few months later, so it would be better to make them more explicit.
- Estimates of the uncertainties in the value of the resonant frequency and the calculated inductance should be quoted.
- The entries are rather cramped — it would be better to space them out more for clarity. In particular, a larger area of graph paper could have been used for plotting the resonance curve, and it could have been attached to a separate page in the notebook.
- A brief 'conclusion' could be included, plus some comments reflecting on any limitations of the experiment or possible improvements.

Q4.1 (a) There will be uncertainties associated with both the measurement of the period and the measurement of the length. The main ones are likely to be:

(i) uncertainty in starting and stopping the stopwatch to coincide with the pendulum passing through a fixed point;

(ii) uncertainty in the calibration of the stopwatch;

(iii) uncertainty of ±1 in the last figure displayed by the digital stopwatch;

(iv) uncertainty in measuring the pendulum's length (i.e. difficulty in locating the centre of mass of the keys, and the need to reposition the metre rule in order to measure 2 m);

(v) uncertainty in reading the scale on the rule;

(vi) uncertainty in the calibration of the rule.

You may have thought of some additional sources of uncertainty, but they are likely to be less significant than those listed above.

(b) Of the six uncertainties listed above, (i), (iii), (iv) and (v) are likely to be *random* uncertainties; (ii) and (vi) will be *systematic* uncertainties. Uncertainty (i) may have a systematic component as well: for example, the student may always be late starting the stopwatch. Uncertainty (iv) may also have a systematic component, e.g. if the length is measured to the point where the keys are attached to the string, rather than to the centre of mass.

Q5.1 (a) The positions of the edges of the strip are at 11.06 cm and 14.90 cm on the scale, so the width is 3.84 cm. By interpolating between the millimetre graduations, the positions can be estimated to ±0.02 cm (or possibly even better if you have good eyesight or make use of a magnifying lens), which means an uncertainty of about ±0.04 cm in the width. So the width is (3.84 ± 0.04) cm. Note that it is essential that you quote an uncertainty with the measured value.

Comment *You will see in Section 6.3 that adding the two uncertainties in this way is somewhat pessimistic, and that the uncertainty in this situation is more realistically quoted as ±0.03 cm.*

(b) The temperature is (82.9 ± 0.1) °C. This scale can be interpolated to the nearest 0.1 °C.

(c) The voltage is (1.46 ± 0.01) V. Again, this scale can be interpolated to 1/10 of a division, i.e. 0.01 V.

(d) The diameter of the coin is (20.36 ± 0.02) mm. The final two digits are determined by looking for the graduation on the vernier scale that most closely aligns with a graduation on the main scale. In this case it is the

3.6 on the vernier scale that appears to align most closely, though the 3.4 and 3.8 are also almost aligned.

In all of these examples, there are likely to be additional uncertainties associated with the measurement, for example, uncertainties in the calibration of the instrument.

Q5.2 (a) The mean value $\langle R \rangle$ is found by adding all of the resistance values and dividing by the number of values (ten). Thus

$$\langle R \rangle = (220\,\Omega)/10 = 22.0\,\Omega.$$

(b) The measurements are spread over a range from 21.6 Ω to 22.3 Ω, a range of about ±0.35 Ω. It is conventional to quote the uncertainty in a measured value as about 2/3 of the spread, in recognition of the fact that values from the extremes of the range are not very likely. So in this case we would estimate the uncertainty as 2/3 × (±0.35 Ω), which is ±0.2 Ω to one significant figure.

(c) The standard deviation is calculated using the procedure in Box 5.1. The mean value was calculated in part (a). The sum of the square deviations of the measurements from the mean is $0.40\,\Omega^2$. The mean of the square deviations is therefore $(0.40\,\Omega^2)/10 = 0.04\,\Omega^2$, and the standard deviation (calculated by taking the square root of this) is 0.2 Ω. Note that the magnitude of the uncertainty estimated in (b) is approximately the same as the standard deviation, and this is why it is often sufficient to use the simpler 2/3-spread procedure.

Q5.3 (a) For random processes, when n events are counted, the uncertainty in that number is $\sqrt{n}$. So in this case the uncertainty is $\sqrt{256} = 16$. The fractional uncertainty is

$$\frac{\sqrt{n}}{n} = \frac{1}{\sqrt{n}} = \frac{1}{16} = 0.0625$$

which is 0.06 to one significant figure. The percentage uncertainty is therefore 100% × 0.06 = 6%.

(b) An uncertainty of 1% corresponds to a fractional uncertainty of 0.01. The number of counts required to achieve this fractional uncertainty is given by $1/\sqrt{n} = 0.01$, i.e. $n = 10\,000$. Since 256 photons were counted in 10 s, the count rate is about 26 photons per second, and so we would need to count for about 10 000/26 seconds to count 10 000 photons, which is a period of about 400 s. So to reduce the uncertainty by a factor of six, we require an increase in the counting time of a factor of about 6^2.

Q5.4 The uncertainties in the calibrations of the stopwatch and the metre rule could be greatly reduced by comparing them with more accurate standards. The stopwatch could be compared with the telephone talking clock, or with radio time signals, over a period of hours. For example, if one hour of the talking clock was measured as 60 minutes and 5.4 seconds, then all times measured with the stopwatch would be corrected by multiplying by 3600.0/3605.4. Similarly, the wooden metre rule could be compared with a more accurate metal rule.

The systematic uncertainties associated with starting and stopping the stopwatch and with measuring the pendulum's length could possibly be reduced. The experimenter could practise the timing and use a reference marker so that they could start and stop the watch as the pendulum passed this marker. They might identify the position of the centre of mass of the keys and measure the length from there. They could also take precautions to ensure that they minimized uncertainties associated with moving the rule when measuring the two-metre length.

Q6.1 (a) The uncertainty s_m in the mean value of n measurements is related to the standard deviation s of the measurements by

$$s_m = \frac{s}{\sqrt{n-1}}. \tag{6.1}$$

So $s_m = 0.006\text{ mm}/\sqrt{10-1} = 0.002$ mm. Note that this is much smaller than the uncertainty in a single measurement, which is represented by the standard deviation of 0.006 mm.

(b) The difference between the mean value (0.785 mm) and the suspected 'true' value (0.791 mm) is 0.006 mm, which is three times larger than the uncertainty in the mean. Assuming that values of the means that would be obtained from many sets of ten measurements are normally distributed, then the probability of the value of the mean differing from the 'true' value by three times the uncertainty in the mean is only 0.3%. It is therefore unlikely (though possible) that the true value is 0.791 mm.

(c) From Equation 6.1, if $s_m = 0.001$ mm, and $s = 0.006$ mm, then $\sqrt{n-1} = 6$, and so $n = 37$.

So reducing the uncertainty from 0.002 mm to 0.001 mm would require about four times as many measurements.

Q6.2 There are three uncertainties to combine to get the overall uncertainty in the voltmeter's reading, but they are all expressed in different ways. To combine them it is simplest to express them all as an uncertainty in the actual voltage reading. Thus

0.015% of reading = (0.015/100) × 30.511 mV = 0.0046 mV;

0.0015% of full scale = (0.0015/100) × 200 mV = 0.003 mV;

1 in final digit = 0.001 mV.

These uncertainties can now be combined using Equation 6.3:

$$\delta X = \sqrt{\delta x_1^2 + \delta x_2^2 + \delta x_3^2}$$

$$= \sqrt{0.0046^2 + 0.003^2 + 0.001^2}\ \text{mV}$$

$$= 0.006\ \text{mV to one significant figure.}$$

So the voltage would be quoted as (30.511 ± 0.006) mV.

Q6.3 The power dissipated is $P = IV = 8.5\ \text{A} \times 12.2\ \text{V} = 103.7\ \text{W}$. The uncertainty in the power is calculated using Equation 6.5 in Table 6.1:

$$\frac{\delta P}{P} = \sqrt{\left(\frac{\delta I}{I}\right)^2 + \left(\frac{\delta V}{V}\right)^2}$$

$$= \sqrt{\left(\frac{0.2}{8.5}\right)^2 + \left(\frac{0.4}{12.2}\right)^2}$$

$$= \sqrt{0.000554 + 0.001075}$$

$$= 0.0404.$$

So $\delta P = 0.0404 \times 103.7\ \text{W} = 4.2\ \text{W}$. The power dissipated should therefore be quoted as (104 ± 4) W.

Comment *Remember that it is common practice to quote the uncertainty to one significant figure. With an uncertainty of ±4 W, there is no point in quoting the power to greater precision than the nearest watt.*

Q6.4 When connected in series, the total resistance is the sum of the individual resistances, so $R = (82 + 330 + 1200)\ \Omega = 1612\ \Omega$. The uncertainty in this value is calculated using Equation 6.12 in Table 6.1:

$$\delta R = \sqrt{(\delta R_1)^2 + (\delta R_2)^2 + (\delta R_3)^2}.$$

The uncertainties in the 330 Ω and 1200 Ω resistances need to be converted to ohms, before substituting into this equation:

$$5\% \times 330\ \Omega = 16.5\ \Omega; \qquad 1\% \times 1200\ \Omega = 12\ \Omega.$$

So $\delta R = \sqrt{5^2 + 16.5^2 + 12^2}\ \Omega = 21.0\ \Omega$. If we quote the uncertainty to one significant figure, then the value of the total resistance is $(1.61 \pm 0.02) \times 10^3\ \Omega$.

Comment *Note that if you omitted the 5 Ω uncertainty from the calculation, then you would get the result δR = 20.4 Ω, which is the same as the value calculated using all three uncertainties to one significant figure. This illustrates an important general point that can simplify uncertainty calculations: you can ignore uncertainties that are smaller than one-third of the largest uncertainty when calculating uncertainties in sums or differences. Similarly, you can ignore fractional uncertainties that are less than one-third of the largest fractional uncertainty when calculating uncertainties in products and ratios.*

Q6.5 Acceleration $a_z = (v_z - u_z)/t$, where v_z and u_z are the final and initial velocities and t is the time period over which the velocity change is measured. So

$$a_z = \frac{(58 - 1.7)\ \text{m s}^{-1}}{5.5\ \text{s}} = \frac{56.3}{5.5}\ \text{m s}^{-2}$$

$$= 10.24\ \text{m s}^{-2}.$$

We determine the uncertainty in the acceleration in two stages. First we find the uncertainty in $(v_z - u_z)$, which we will call $\Delta(v_z - u_z)$, and since this involves a difference we use Equation 6.4 in Table 6.1. This uncertainty is

$$\sqrt{0.5^2 + 1^2}\ \text{m s}^{-1} = \sqrt{1.25}\ \text{m s}^{-1} = 1.1\ \text{m s}^{-1}.$$

The second step is to combine this uncertainty with the timing uncertainty, and since this involves a ratio we use Equation 6.5:

$$\frac{\delta a_z}{a_z} = \sqrt{\left(\frac{\Delta(v_z - u_z)}{v_z - u_z}\right)^2 + \left(\frac{\Delta t}{t}\right)^2}$$

$$= \sqrt{\left(\frac{1.1}{56.3}\right)^2 + \left(\frac{0.2}{5.5}\right)^2}$$

$$= \sqrt{0.00038 + 0.00132}$$

$$= 0.041.$$

Thus $\delta a_z = 0.041 \times 10.24\ \text{m s}^{-2} = 0.42\ \text{m s}^{-2}$, and the mean acceleration is therefore $(10.2 \pm 0.4)\ \text{m s}^{-2}$.

Q6.6 The wavelength is given by

$$\lambda = d \sin\theta = 1.655 \times 10^{-6}\ \text{m} \times \sin 24.1° = 6.758 \times 10^{-7}\ \text{m}.$$

To find the uncertainty in this value, we first calculate the uncertainty in the function $\sin\theta$ by evaluating $\sin(24.1° + 0.1°) = 0.4099$ and $\sin(24.1°) = 0.4083$. The difference between these values is 0.0016, so the uncertainty in $\sin\theta$ is $\delta(\sin\theta) = \pm 0.0016$.

We then combine this uncertainty with the uncertainty in d, and since this involves the product $d \sin\theta$ we use Equation 6.5:

$$\frac{\delta\lambda}{\lambda} = \sqrt{\left(\frac{\delta d}{d}\right)^2 + \left(\frac{\delta(\sin\theta)}{\sin\theta}\right)^2}$$

$$= \sqrt{\left(\frac{0.005}{1.655}\right)^2 + \left(\frac{0.0016}{0.408}\right)^2}$$

$$= \sqrt{0.91 \times 10^{-5} + 1.54 \times 10^{-5}}$$

$$= 0.00495.$$

So $\delta\lambda = 0.00495 \times 6.758 \times 10^{-7}\ \text{m} = 0.033 \times 10^{-7}\ \text{m}$, and the wavelength is therefore $(6.76 \pm 0.03) \times 10^{-7}$ m.

Q8.1 If you managed to list 7 to 10 points where the student has departed from good practice, then you are doing well. We won't give a list of points here. Instead, we suggest that you read the guidelines for plotting graphs in Section 8.1 and for using uncertainty bars in Section 8.2, and then try this question again in order to identify any points that you missed the first time.

Q8.2 The three data points and their uncertainty bars are plotted in Figure 8.13. For point (b), the percentage uncertainties have to be converted to absolute values of volts and amps before they can be plotted: ±5% of 2.9 volts is ±0.15 volts, and ±10% of 4.1 amps is ±0.4 amps, to one significant figure. No horizontal bar is shown for point (c), because the uncertainty is too small to draw a bar of the appropriate size.

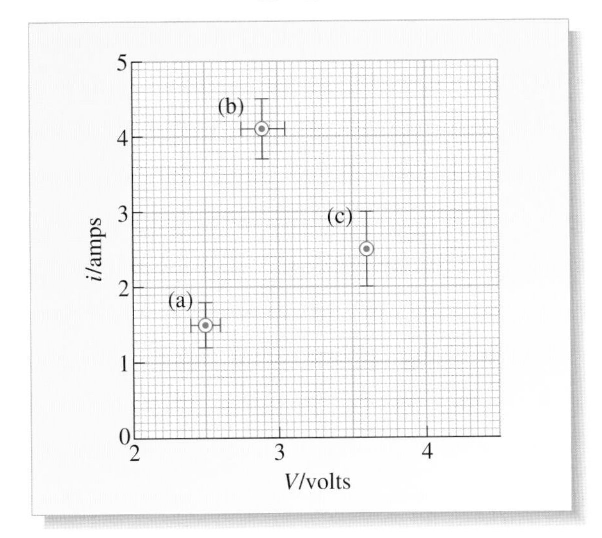

Figure 8.13 Answer to Question 8.2: three data points and their uncertainty bars.

Q8.3 Ten points that you might have listed are:

- there is no caption or title to indicate what has been plotted; a possible caption might be 'Figure 1: Dependence of photocell stopping voltage on frequency of light';
- the independent variable (in this case, the frequency) is generally plotted on the *horizontal* axis;
- the unit (Hz) is missing from the label on the frequency axis;
- the power of ten (10^{14}) is also missing from the label on the frequency axis; this axis should be labelled 'frequency/10^{14} Hz';
- the name and/or symbol for the variable plotted on the horizontal axis has been omitted; this axis should be labelled 'stopping voltage/volts';
- the choice of scale on the horizontal axis (1 cm on the graph paper equivalent to 0.125 V) would have made it difficult to plot the points; plotting is easiest if each division on the graph paper represents 1, or 2, or 5 multiplied by an appropriate power of ten; in this case, 1 cm = 0.1 V, or 1 cm = 0.2 V would have been simpler scales to use;
- only a limited range of the vertical scale has been used; it would have been better to suppress the zero on this scale and only plot the range from 4 to 8 ($\times 10^{14}$ Hz);
- the symbols used to plot the points are rather large and untidy; a small cross or a dot with a small circle around it would have been better;
- the general trend of the data should be indicated by a straight line or a smooth curve, rather than by drawing a zigzag line connecting the data points;
- uncertainty bars could have been plotted to indicate the uncertainty of ±0.04 V in the values of stopping voltage; the uncertainties in the frequencies ($\pm 0.005 \times 10^{14}$ Hz) are too small to plot on the graph.

The results of the experiment have been replotted in Figure 8.14 to rectify the shortcomings listed above.

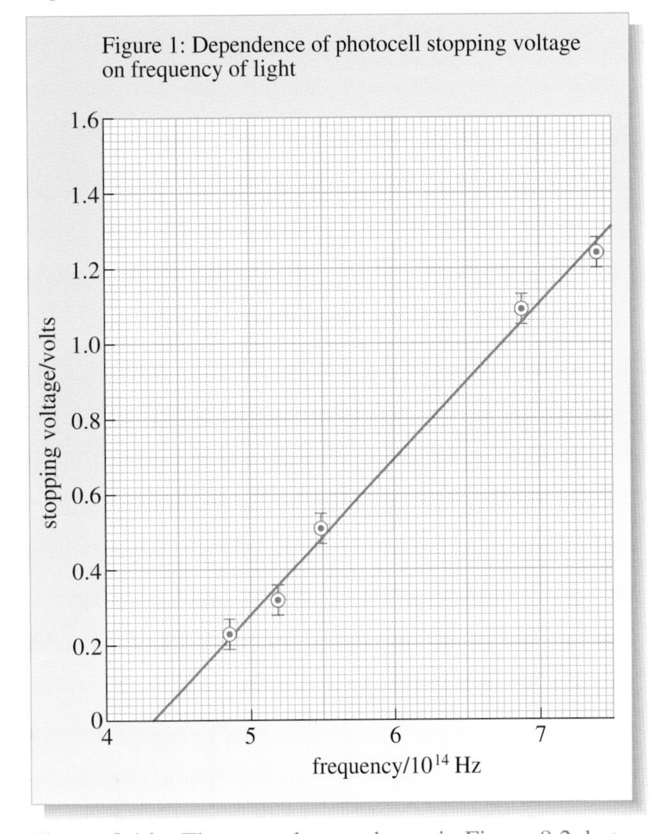

Figure 8.14 The same data as shown in Figure 8.2, but replotted according to the guidelines for graph plotting in Section 8.1. Note that the graph has been squashed to fit into the column width; the scales on both axes should be expanded by a factor of two when the graph is plotted during an experiment.

Q8.4 (a) Our estimate of the best-fit line is shown as the black line in Figure 8.15. Note that the points are fairly equally distributed above and below this line, and that the line intersects all but two of the uncertainty bars. The gradient of the line is

$$[(1.50 - 1.09) \times 10^5\,\text{Pa}]/(100 - 0)\,°\text{C} = 410\,\text{Pa}\,°\text{C}^{-1},$$

and the intercept is 1.09×10^5 Pa. Remember that it is important to include units as part of the gradient and intercept values.

(b) The coloured lines in Figure 8.15 are our estimates of the lines with maximum and minimum gradients that are compatible with the data. They both pass through about two-thirds of the uncertainty bars. The gradients of the two lines are 510 Pa °C^{-1} and 330 Pa °C^{-1}, so the uncertainty in the gradient is

$$\pm 0.5(510 - 330)\,\text{Pa}\,°\text{C}^{-1} = \pm 90\,\text{Pa}\,°\text{C}^{-1}.$$

The intercepts of the two lines are 1.12×10^5 Pa and 1.05×10^5 Pa, so the uncertainty in the intercept is $\pm 0.5(1.12 - 1.05) \times 10^5\,\text{Pa} = \pm 0.035 \times 10^5$ Pa, or $\pm 0.04 \times 10^5$ Pa to one significant figure.

Drawing the lines with maximum and minimum gradients is not an exact science, so the uncertainties that you derived from your lines may differ from the values calculated above by up to 30%.

(c) The general equation of a straight line is $y = mx + c$, where y is the variable plotted on the vertical axis, x is the variable plotted on the horizontal axis, m is the gradient and c is the intercept with the vertical axis. So for Figure 8.15, P is equivalent to y and θ is equivalent to x. The equation representing the data is therefore

$$P = (4.1 \pm 0.9) \times 10^2\,\text{Pa}\,°\text{C}^{-1} \times \theta + (1.09 \pm 0.04) \times 10^5\,\text{Pa}.$$

Q8.5 (a) If we rearrange the equation $PV = nRT$ so that the variables P and V are on opposite sides, we get

$$P = nRT\left(\frac{1}{V}\right).$$

Plotting P against $1/V$ should give a straight line that passes through the origin and has gradient nRT.

(b) Since $P = RI^2$, plotting P against I^2 should give a straight line through the origin, with gradient R.

(c) Since we do not know the value of λ we cannot plot a graph of P versus $e^{-z/\lambda}$. However, if we take the natural logarithm of each side of the equation, then we get

$$\begin{aligned}\log_e P &= \log_e(P_0\,e^{-z/\lambda})\\ &= \log_e P_0 + \log_e(e^{-z/\lambda})\\ &= \log_e P_0 - z/\lambda.\end{aligned}$$

Plotting $\log_e P$ against z should therefore give a straight line with gradient $-1/\lambda$ and intercept $\log_e P_0$.

Q9.1 (a) Figure 9.4 shows a graph plotted with the Microsoft Excel spreadsheet application. Note that the zero was suppressed on the vertical scale, since otherwise all of the data points would have been in the top 15% of resistance range displayed on the graph.

(b) A straight line was fitted to the graph and its equation is displayed in Figure 9.4, in the form $y = mx + c$. In this case y (the variable plotted on the vertical axis) corresponds to the resistance R and x corresponds to the temperature θ. So the (incomplete) equation is:

$$R = 0.1141\theta + 27.592.$$

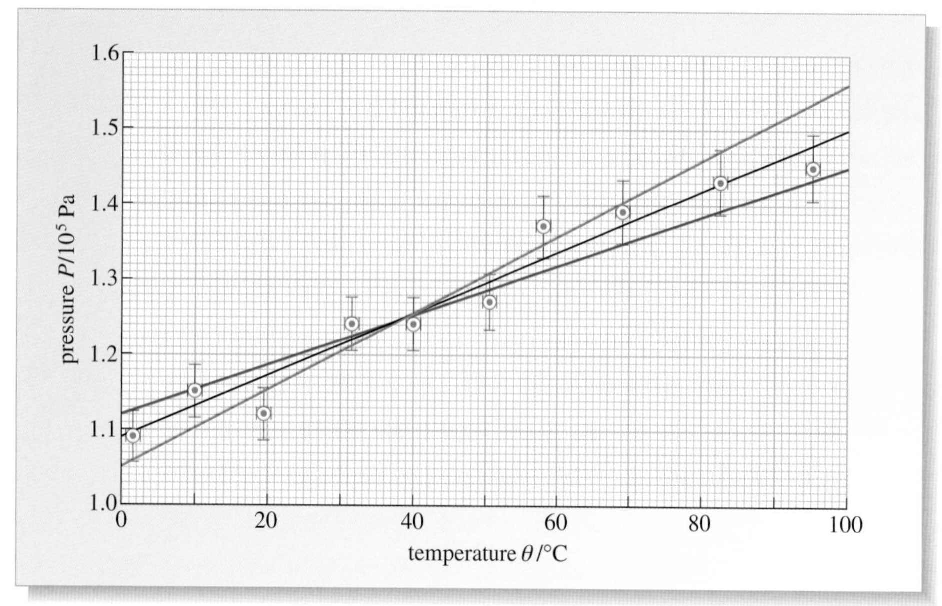

Figure 8.15 Answer to Question 8.4. Best-fit straight line (black) and lines of maximum gradient (red) and minimum gradient (purple) for the pressure versus temperature data.

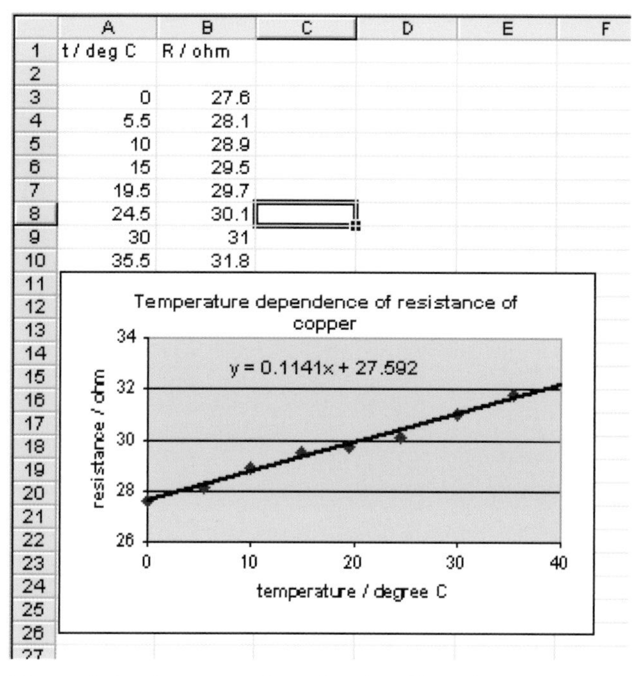

	A	B	C	D	E	F
1	t / deg C	R / ohm				
2						
3	0	27.6				
4	5.5	28.1				
5	10	28.9				
6	15	29.5				
7	19.5	29.7				
8	24.5	30.1				
9	30	31				
10	35.5	31.8				

Figure 9.4 Answer to Question 9.1. Note that we have used t in the spreadsheet rather than θ, because we can't enter Greek letters in the spreadsheet.

This equation is not yet complete — it requires some units for the gradient and the intercept. The unit of the intercept with the vertical (resistance) axis must be ohm, and the unit of the gradient must be ohm/°C, since the gradient (= rise/run) is a ratio of the quantity plotted vertically and the quantity plotted horizontally. Also, since the data has only three significant figures, the numerical values of the constants can be rounded to three significant figures.
So the complete equation is:

$$R = (0.114\,\text{ohm}\,°\text{C}^{-1}) \times \theta + 27.6\,\text{ohm}.$$

Q9.2 (a) The mean of the ten measurements is 786.6 μm.

(b) The standard deviation s is 3.0 μm.

(c) The uncertainty of the mean, s_m, is related to the standard deviation s by the expression

$$s_m = \frac{s}{\sqrt{n-1}}.$$

Thus

$$s_m = \frac{3.0}{\sqrt{10-1}}\,\mu\text{m} = 1.0\,\mu\text{m}.$$